W9-CDC-657

Hold fast to
Dreams

Hold fast to Dreams

Poems Old & New Selected by
Arna Bontemps

Follett Publishing Company
Chicago · New York

BRIAR CLIFF COLLEGE
LIBRARY

SIOUX CITY, IOWA

Copyright acknowledgments begin on page 189

Copyright © 1969 by Arna Bontemps. All rights reserved. No portion of this book may be reproduced in any form without written permission from the publisher. Manufactured in the United States of America. Published simultaneously in Canada by The Ryerson Press, Toronto.

ISBN 0 695 43770 8 Titan binding
ISBN 0 695 83770 9 Trade binding

Library of Congress Catalog Number: 69-15764

Second Printing

PS
586
.B58

To Cecile & Gwendolyn

61260

CONTENTS

DREAM VARIATIONS

DREAMS * LANGSTON HUGHES   19

TRIFLE * GEORGIA DOUGLAS JOHNSON   20

THE BLUE RIDGE * HARRIET MONROE   20

A PECK OF GOLD * ROBERT FROST   21

TO MAKE A PRAIRIE * EMILY DICKINSON   21

LA BELLE DAME SANS MERCI * JOHN KEATS   22

SON * JAMES A. EMANUEL   24

TRAVEL * ROBERT LOUIS STEVENSON   26

PAPER BOATS * RABINDRANATH TAGORE   28

I DREAM A WORLD * LANGSTON HUGHES   29

WHEN DAWN COMES TO THE CITY * CLAUDE MCKAY   30

IF YOU SHOULD GO * COUNTEE CULLEN   32

I HEAR AMERICA SINGING

THE GRASS ON THE MOUNTAIN * MARY AUSTIN   34

THE NEW COLOSSUS * EMMA LAZARUS   35

NIGHT JOURNEY * THEODORE ROETHKE   36

HANDS OF A BROWN WOMAN * F. MARSHALL DAVIS   37

AMERICA * CLAUDE MCKAY   40

MY CITY * JAMES WELDON JOHNSON   41

MANHOLE COVERS * KARL SHAPIRO   42

TRAVEL * EDNA ST. VINCENT MILLAY   43

REFUGEE IN AMERICA * LANGSTON HUGHES   44

SPRING THUNDER

SPRING THUNDER * MARK VAN DOREN   46

SPRING REMINISCENCE * COUNTEE CULLEN   47

I WANDERED LONELY AS A CLOUD * WILLIAM WORDSWORTH   48

Rainy Song * max eastman 49

After Winter * sterling brown 50

Spring in New Hampshire * claude mckay 52

Spring Grass * carl sandburg 53

Reconnaissance * arna bontemps 54

My Heart Leaps Up When I Behold * william wordsworth 55

The Unknown * countee cullen 55

Nothing Gold Can Stay * robert frost 56

THE SOUND OF TREES

The Sound of Trees * robert frost 58

Tree at My Window * robert frost 59

The Poplar * richard aldington 60

Leaves * countee cullen 62

City Trees * edna st. vincent millay 64

Wild Plum * orrick johns 65

A Tree Design * arna bontemps 66

BATS, LOONS, AND OTHER CREATURES

The Bats * witter bynner 68

The Mountain and the Squirrel * ralph waldo emerson 69

The Fox and the Grapes * joseph lauren 70

Four Little Foxes * lew sarett 71

Twelfth Night: Song of the Camels * elizabeth coatsworth 72

The Blind Men and the Elephant * john godfrey saxe 73

The Loon * lew sarett 75

To a Winter Squirrel * gwendolyn brooks 76

SEA FEVER

Sea Born * harold vinal 78

Sailor * langston hughes 80

Sea Shell * amy lowell 81

The Golden City of St. Mary * john masefield 82

Sketch * carl sandburg 83

I Thought It Was Tangiers I Wanted * langston hughes 84

Trade Winds * john masefield 86

WINNERS AND LOSERS

Saturday's Child * countee cullen 88

Tangerines * alexander karanikas 89

To James * frank horne 90

No Images * waring cuney 92

A Black Man Talks of Reaping * arna bontemps 93

The Frogs Who Wanted a King * joseph lauren 94

When I Was One-and-Twenty * a. e. housman 96

The Winning of the TV West * john t. alexander 97

Casey at the Bat * ernest lawrence thayer 98

A Song in the Front Yard * gwendolyn brooks 101

Conquest * georgia douglas johnson 102

We Wear the Mask * paul laurence dunbar 103

John Henry * anonymous 104

We Real Cool * gwendolyn brooks 106

Youth * langston hughes 107

Arithmetic * carl sandburg 108

Kid Stuff * frank horne 109

HOW DO I LOVE THEE?

How Do I Love Thee? * elizabeth barrett browning 112

We'll Go No More A-Roving * byron, lord george gordon 113

A Red, Red Rose * robert burns 114

Song to Celia * ben jonson 115

Patterns * amy lowell 116

The River-Merchant's Wife: A Letter * ezra pound   120

Sonnet CXXX * william shakespeare   122

Night Song at Amalfi * sara teasdale   123

The Look * sara teasdale   124

Music, When Soft Voices Die * percy bysshe shelley   124

AFTER AUGUST

Autumn Flight * alexander karanikas   126

Autumn * emily dickinson   127

Let It Be Forgotten * sara teasdale   127

The Golden Tickseed * gustav davidson   128

The Reunion * owen dodson   129

My November Guest * robert frost   130

The House on the Hill * e.a. robinson   131

Banking Coal * jean toomer   132

The Dark Hills * e.a. robinson   133

The Last Leaf * oliver wendell holmes   134

Overtones * william alexander percy   136

The Crazy Woman * gwendolyn brooks   136

STRONG MEN

Strong Men * sterling a. brown   138

Not in Vain * emily dickinson   140

Epitaphs: For Paul Laurence Dunbar * countee cullen   141

Mercy * william shakespeare   141

A Man's a Man for A' That * robert burns   142

The Man With the Hoe * edwin markham   144

Fishermen * james a. emanuel   146

Now That He Is Safely Dead * carl w. hines, jr.   147

Abraham Lincoln Walks at Midnight * vachel lindsay   148

Stanley Meets Mutesa * james d. rubadiri   150

THE POET AND HIS SONG

The Poet and His Song * paul laurence dunbar 154

Rhapsody * william stanley braithwaite 156

Requiem * robert louis stevenson 157

O Daedalus, Fly Away Home * robert hayden 158

A Song * paul laurence dunbar 160

Smells * christopher morley 161

The Bells * edgar allan poe 162

The Jazz of This Hotel * vachel lindsay 166

The Tropics in New York * claude mckay 167

Ars Poetica * archibald macleish 168

Your World * georgia douglas johnson 170

Literary Love * harry kemp 170

NOTHING HAPPENS ONLY ONCE

Circle One * owen dodson 172

Anthem for Doomed Youth * wilfred owen 173

Ballade by the Fire * e.a. robinson 174

The Debt * paul laurence dunbar 176

Mother to Son * langston hughes 177

The Treehouse * james a. emanuel 178

Dirge * william shakespeare 179

INDEXES

Authors 180

Titles 182

First Lines 185

Acknowledgments 189

On Integrating the Old With the New

A little-known poet once wrote some well-known lines in which he said, among other things,

MAKE NEW FRIENDS, BUT KEEP THE OLD;
THOSE ARE SILVER, THESE ARE GOLD.

If this is a good rule for friendship, it seems to me it might be equally good when applied to poems. In either case, we notice that the old friend and the new poem have something in common, even if it is no more than that each is recognized on sight and not likely to be mistaken for another. A vague, half-remembered friend can hardly be considered a friend at all, and a poem we cannot recall doesn't mean much to us either.

Much has been said or written about the enjoyment of poetry; some of it tremendously wise, some of it not. But the comment I like best came from a favorite modern composer when he was asked to define *rhythm*. Wrinkling his forehead and hesitating, he finally blurted hopelessly, "If you have to ask, you haven't got it."

I feel somewhat the same about what makes us enjoy poetry. You may have a dead nerve where such things are concerned, and if so it is just your bad luck. However, if you already like music and stories and the magic of words, you may be able to increase your enjoyment.

I have often thought it possible to hurt a poem by talking about it too much. Poetry is meant to be read or said. All of it can be divided into two kinds: the poetry we remember and the poetry we forget. I started this collection with poems I couldn't forget. Then I added others that seemed to go well with the older poems.

The first time I read Waring Cuney's "No Images" or Witter Bynner's "Bats" or Langston Hughes' "I Thought it Was Tangiers I Wanted" I knew at once that these were poems I would want to keep in my memory the rest of my life, along with the older ones I had read or learned in school.

I am not ashamed of enjoying poems sometimes considered familiar or old-fashioned. It does not keep me from liking new poems anymore than the enjoyment of old music makes me turn my back on the latest sounds in music. More often I think it helps. If you once get the poetry bug, you may be surprised to discover how much there is to enjoy, both new and old, how many kinds. You may also be surprised to find how many times some poems may be read before you feel you have had enough of them. Often, I would guess, as many times as you would play a record.

All people need poetry and must have it in order to stay alive and endure the hardships as well as the high moments of life. What is satisfying and helpful to one, however, may not be what another needs. If one responds only to singing commercials and perhaps lines scribbled on walls, we may decide he has that dead nerve. Even so, in one way or another, he is likely to give himself away. He cannot get along without something *like* poetry, even if it is not the real thing.

Those of us to whom poetry has been important for a long time and who admit that nothing ever quite takes its place are naturally concerned about those who don't seem to get the message. We try to think of things to tell them that will awaken their interest, but I would rather take a chance on waiting for them to awaken themselves.

ARNA BONTEMPS
CHICAGO, 1969

Hold fast to
Dreams

Dream
Variations

DREAMS

Hold fast to dreams
For if dreams die
Life is a broken-winged bird
That cannot fly.

Hold fast to dreams
For when dreams go
Life is a barren field
Frozen with snow.

LANGSTON HUGHES

TRIFLE

Against the day of sorrow
Lay by some trifling thing
A smile, a kiss, a flower
For sweet remembering.

Then when the day is darkest
Without one rift of blue
Take out your little trifle
And dream your dream anew.

GEORGIA DOUGLAS JOHNSON

THE BLUE RIDGE

Still and calm,
In purple robes of kings,
The low-lying mountains sleep at the edge of the world.
The forests cover them like mantles;
Day and night
Rise and fall over them like the wash of waves.

Asleep, they reign.
Silent, they say all.
Hush me, O slumbering mountains—
Send me dreams.

HARRIET MONROE

A PECK OF GOLD

Dust always blowing about the town,
Except when sea-fog laid it down,
And I was one of the children told
Some of the blowing dust was gold.

All the dust the wind blew high
Appeared like gold in the sunset sky,
But I was one of the children told
Some of the dust was really gold.

Such was life in the Golden Gate:
Gold dusted all we drank and ate,
And I was one of the children told,
"We all must eat our peck of gold."

ROBERT FROST

TO MAKE A PRAIRIE

To make a prairie it takes a clover and one bee—
One clover, and a bee
And reverie.
The reverie alone will do
If bees are few.

EMILY DICKINSON

La Belle Dame Sans Merci

O what can ail thee, knight-at-arms,
  Alone and palely loitering?
The sedge has withered from the lake,
  And no birds sing.

O what can ail thee, knight-at-arms,
  So haggard and so woebegone?
The squirrel's granary is full,
  And the harvest's done.

I see a lily on thy brow
  With anguish moist and fever dew.
And on thy cheeks a fading rose
  Fast withereth too.

I met a lady in the meads,
  Full beautiful—a faery's child,
Her hair was long, her foot was light,
  And her eyes were wild.

I made a garland for her head,
  And bracelets too, and fragrant zone;
She looked at me as she did love,
  And made sweet moan.

I set her on my pacing steed
  And nothing else saw all day long.
For sidelong would she bend, and sing
  A faery's song.

She found me roots of relish sweet,
  And honey wild, and manna dew,
And sure in language strange she said—
  "I love thee true."

She took me to her elfin grot,
  And there she wept, and sighed full sore,
And there I shut her wild wild eyes
  With kisses four.

And there she lulled me asleep,
  And there I dreamed—Ah! woe betide!
The latest dream I ever dreamed
  On the cold hill's side.

I saw pale kings and princes too,
  Pale warriors, death-pale were they all;
They cried—"La Belle Dame sans Merci
  Hath thee in thrall!"

I saw their starved lips in the gloom,
  With horrid warning gapèd wide,
And I awoke and found me here,
  On the cold hill's side.

And this is why I sojourn here,
  Alone and palely loitering,
Though the sedge is withered from the lake
  And no birds sing.

JOHN KEATS

SON

Cross-legged on his bed,
The President is twelve,
Signaling to order all his crew:
Himself as Treasurer, Chief Spy,
Keeper of the Chemicals,
And only member, too.

The minutes of Club Fantastic
    tell it all:
The Indianheads his paper route
    turned up for dues.
The four-way-grid code messages
    he found in shoes,
The fingerprints and buttons
    marked in basement hush,
The friends he filed away in
    "Sent by Thrush."

Barefoot at the desk no one
    disturbs,
The President nods over geometry
    and German verbs
And Orwell's *1984*, all done.
What can a President do—
Or Treasurer, Chief Spy, Keeper
    of the Chemicals too—
When all of his fantastic crew,
Despite all signals, doze as one?

Founder of the Club, mystery of
  twelve,
How signal to you? How softly
  delve
Into your lonely sleep, that even
  there, even you
Might close hands with this
  crew?

JAMES A. EMANUEL

TRAVEL

I should like to rise and go
Where the golden apples grow;
Where below another sky
Parrot Islands anchored lie,
And, watched by cockatoos and goats,
Lonely Crusoes building boats;
Where in sunshine reaching out
Eastern cities, miles about,
Are with mosque and minaret
Among sandy gardens set,
And the rich goods from near and far
Hang for sale in the bazaar;
Where the Great Wall round China goes,
And on one side the desert blows,
And with bell and voice and drum,
Cities on the other hum;
Where are forests, hot as fire,
Wide as England, tall as a spire,
Full of apes and coconuts
And the Negro hunters' huts;
Where the knotty crocodile
Lies and blinks in the Nile,
And the red flamingo flies
Hunting fish before his eyes;

Where in jungles, near and far,
Man-devouring tigers are,
Lying close and giving ear
Lest the hunt be drawing near,
Or a comer-by be seen
Swinging in a palanquin;
Where among the desert sands
Some deserted city stands,
All its children, sweep and prince,
Grown to manhood ages since,
Not a foot in street or house,
Not a stir of child or mouse,
And when kindly falls the night,
In all the town no spark of light.
There I'll come when I'm a man
With a camel caravan;
Light a fire in the gloom
Of some dusty dining room;
See the pictures on the walls,
Heroes, fights, and festivals;
And in a corner find the toys
Of the old Egyptian boys.

ROBERT LOUIS STEVENSON

Paper Boats

Day by day I float my paper boats one by one down the
running stream.
In big black letters I write my name on them and the
name of the village where I live.
I hope that someone in some strange land will find them
and know who I am.
I load my little boats with *shiuli* flowers from our garden,
and hope that these blooms of dawn will be carried
safely to land in the night.
I launch my paper boats and look up into the sky and
see the little clouds setting their white bulging sails.
I know not what playmate of mine in the sky sends them
down the air to race with my boats!
When night comes I bury my face in my arms and dream
that my paper boats float on and on under the midnight stars.
The fairies of sleep are sailing in them, and the lading is
their baskets full of dreams.

RABINDRANATH TAGORE

I DREAM A WORLD

I dream a world where man
No other will scorn,
Where love will bless the earth
And peace its paths adorn.
I dream a world where all
Will know sweet freedom's way,
Where greed no longer saps the soul
Nor avarice blights our day.
A world I dream where black or white,
Whatever race you be,
Will share the bounties of the earth
And every man is free,
Where wretchedness will hang its head,
And joy, like a pearl,
Attend the needs of all mankind.
Of such I dream—
Our world!

LANGSTON HUGHES

When Dawn Comes to the City

The tired cars go grumbling by,
The moaning, groaning cars,
And the old milk carts go rumbling by
Under the same dull stars.
Out of the tenements, cold as stone,
Dark figures start for work;
I watch them sadly shuffle on,
'Tis dawn, dawn in New York.

But I would be on the island of the sea,
In the heart of the island of the sea,
Where the cocks are crowing, crowing, crowing,
And the hens are cackling in the rose-apple tree,
Where the old draft horse is neighing, neighing,
neighing
Out on the brown dew-silvered lawn,
And the tethered cow is lowing, lowing, lowing,
And dear old Ned is braying, braying, braying,
And the shaggy Nannie goat is calling, calling,
calling

From her little trampled corner of the long
wide lea
That stretches to the waters of the hill stream
falling
Sheer upon the flat rocks joyously!
There, oh there! on the island of the sea,
There I would be at dawn.

The tired cars go grumbling by,
The crazy, lazy cars,
And the same milk carts go rumbling by
Under the dying stars.
A lonely newsboy hurries by,
Humming a recent ditty;
Red streaks strike through the gray of the sky,
The dawn comes to the city.

But I would be on the island of the sea,
In the heart of the island of the sea,
Where the cocks are crowing, crowing, crowing,
And the hens are cackling in the rose-apple tree,
Where the old draft horse is neighing, neighing,
neighing
Out on the brown dew-silvered lawn,
And the tethered cow is lowing, lowing, lowing,
And dear old Ned is braying, braying, braying,
And the shaggy Nannie goat is calling, calling,
calling
From her little trampled corner of the long
wide lea
That stretches to the waters of the hill stream
falling
Sheer upon the flat rocks joyously!
There, oh there! on the island of the sea,
There I would be at dawn.

CLAUDE MCKAY

31

If You Should Go

Love, leave me like the light,
 The gently passing day;
We would not know, but for the night,
 When it has slipped away.

Go quietly; a dream,
 When done, should leave no trace
That it has lived, except a gleam
 Across the dreamer's face.

COUNTEE CULLEN

I Hear America Singing

The Grass on the Mountain

Oh, long long
The snow has possessed the mountains.

The deer have come down and the bighorn,
They have followed the sun to the south
To feed on the mesquite pods and the bunch grass.
Loud are the thunderdrums
In the tents of the mountains.
Oh, long long
Have we eaten chia seeds
And dried deer's flesh of the summer killing.
We are wearied of our huts
And the smoky smell of our garments.

We are sick with desire of the sun
And the grass on the mountain.

FROM THE PAIUTE AMERICAN INDIAN
TRANSCRIBED BY MARY AUSTIN

THE NEW COLOSSUS

ENGRAVED ON A PLAQUE IN THE STATUE OF LIBERTY

Not like the brazen giant of Greek fame,
With conquering limbs astride from land to land;
Here at our sea-washed, sunset gates shall stand
A mighty woman with a torch, whose flame
Is the imprisoned lightning, and her name
Mother of Exiles. From her beacon-hand
Glows world-wide welcome; her mild eyes command
The air-bridged harbor that twin cities frame.
"Keep, ancient lands, your storied pomp!" cries she
With silent lips. "Give me your tired, your poor,
Your huddled masses yearning to breathe free,
The wretched refuse of your teeming shore.
Send these, the homeless, tempest-tost to me,
I lift my lamp beside the golden door!"

EMMA LAZARUS

NIGHT JOURNEY

Now as the train bears west,
Its rhythm rocks the earth,
And from my Pullman berth
I stare into the night
While others take their rest.
Bridges of iron lace,
A suddenness of trees,
A lap of mountain mist
All cross my line of sight,
Then a bleak wasted place,
And a lake below my knees.
Full on my neck I feel
The straining at a curve;
My muscles move with steel,
I wake in every nerve.
I watch a beacon swing
From dark to blazing bright;
We thunder through ravines
And gullies washed with light.
Beyond the mountain pass
Mist deepens on the pane;
We rush into a rain
That rattles double glass.
Wheels shake the roadbed stone,
The pistons jerk and shove,
I stay up half the night
To see the land I love.

THEODORE ROETHKE

HANDS OF A BROWN WOMAN

FOR A QUARTET OF TWO GUITARS,
A BANJO, AND A TOM-TOM

Your hands, Mandy Lou
(At night, under June trees,
when the gray moonlight
spills through green leaves
and paints your hands
a brown
the color of newly plowed earth)
chant to me whole histories
of the sensuous African jungle
    before You were You
    and I was I.

Your hands
build brown jungle huts
    with the memories they hold.

Hands, (brown, even as yours)
    have loosed long straight arrows
    that struck
    suddenly,
    quick as the fangs of the African cobra,
    deep into the hearts
    of the lion, the leopard, the antelope.

Hands, (brown, even as yours)
  have held six-foot spears
  that plunged deep into the hearts
  of other men with brown hands—
  relentless
  like the paws of the Great Cats
  have plunged deep
  into the quivering flesh
  of small jungle hares.

Hands, (brown, even as yours)
  have had ten fingers tighten
  to crush
  the soft dark neck
  of an enemy
  even as the giant python
  has felt his great coils tighten
  about the carcass
  of some luckless beast
  in the deep green forests
  of the Congo.

Yet
Hands, (brown, even as yours)
  have caressed sensitive cheeks
  of lovers, husbands, sweethearts
  of hunters, warriors, fighters
  and have insinuated sweet things
  understood by them alone.

Hands, (brown, even as yours)
have held small dark children
and have reprimanded
because of some childish prank.

Brown hands
Were with the Pharaohs in Egypt
Were with Cheops at the pyramids
Went with Christ to Golgotha.
Brown hands
And the white hands
Of Columbus, Cortes,
Laid stones for the foundation
Of a New World.

The sky is an inverted bowl of blue china
So—
Brown hands pluck white cotton
from a sea of plants
even as brown New England rocks
pluck white foam
from a gray December Atlantic.

The hands of you
Mandy Lou
have ten brown fingers
and many tales to tell . . .

F. MARSHALL DAVIS

America

Although she feeds me bread of bitterness,
And sinks into my throat her tiger's tooth,
Stealing my breath of life, I will confess
I love this cultured hell that tests my youth!
Her vigor flows like tides into my blood,
Giving me strength erect against her hate.
Her bigness sweeps my being like a flood.
Yet as a rebel fronts a king in state,
I stand within her walls with not a shred
Of terror, malice, not a word of jeer.
Darkly I gaze into the days ahead,
And see her might and granite wonders there,
Beneath the touch of Time's unerring hand,
Like priceless treasures sinking in the sand.

CLAUDE MCKAY

MY CITY

When I come down to sleep death's endless night,
The threshold of the unknown dark to cross,
What to me then will be the keenest loss,
When this bright world blurs on my fading sight?
Will it be that no more I shall see the trees
Or smell the flowers or hear the singing bird
Or watch the flashing streams or patient herds?
No, I am sure it will be none of these.

But, ah! Manhattan's sights and sounds, her smells,
Her crowds, her throbbing force, the thrill that comes
From being of her a part, her subtle spells,
Her shining towers, her avenues, her slums—
O God! the stark, unutterable pity,
To be dead, and never again behold my city!

JAMES WELDON JOHNSON

MANHOLE COVERS

The beauty of manhole covers—what of that?
Like medals struck by a great savage khan,
Like Mayan calendar stones, unliftable, indecipherable,
Not like old electrum, chased and scored,
Mottoed and sculptured to a turn,
But notched and whelked and pocked and smashed
With the great company names:
Gentle Bethlehem, smiling United States.
This rustproof artifact of my street,
Long after roads are melted away, will lie
Sidewise in the grave of the iron-old world,
Bitten at the edges,
Strong with its cryptic American,
Its dated beauty.

KARL SHAPIRO

TRAVEL

The railroad track is miles away,
  And the day is loud with voices speaking,
Yet there isn't a train goes by all day
  But I hear its whistle shrieking.

All night there isn't a train goes by,
  Though the night is still for sleep and dreaming
But I see its cinders red on the sky,
  And hear its engine steaming.

My heart is warm with the friends I make,
  And better friends I'll not be knowing;
Yet there isn't a train I wouldn't take,
  No matter where it's going.

EDNA ST. VINCENT MILLAY

REFUGEE IN AMERICA

There are words like *Freedom*
Sweet and wonderful to say.
On my heart-strings freedom sings
All day every day.

There are words like *Liberty*
That almost make me cry.
If you had known what I knew
You would know why.

LANGSTON HUGHES

Spring Thunder

Spring Thunder

Listen. The wind is still,
And far away in the night—
See! The uplands fill
With a running light.

Open the doors. It is warm;
And where the sky was clear—
Look! The head of a storm
That marches here!

Come under the trembling hedge—
Fast, although you fumble.
There! Did you hear the edge
Of winter crumble?

MARK VAN DOREN

Spring Reminiscence

"My sweet," you sang,
and, "Sweet," I sang,
  And sweet we sang together,
Glad to be young as the world was young,
  Two colts too strong for a tether.

Shall ever a spring be like that spring,
  Or apple blossoms as white;
Or ever clover smell like the clover
  We lay upon that night?

Shall ever your hand lie in my hand,
  Pulsing to it, I wonder;
Or have the gods, being jealous gods,
  Envied us our thunder?

COUNTEE CULLEN

I WANDERED LONELY AS A CLOUD

I wandered lonely as a cloud
That floats on high o'er vales and hills,
When all at once I saw a crowd—
A host of golden daffodils
Beside the lake, beneath the trees,
Fluttering and dancing in the breeze.

Continuous as the stars that shine
And twinkle on the Milky Way,
They stretched in never-ending line
Along the margin of a bay:
Ten thousand saw I, at a glance,
Tossing their heads in sprightly dance.

The waves beside them danced, but they
Outdid the sparkling waves in glee;
A poet could not be but gay
In such a jocund company;
I gazed—and gazed—but little thought
What wealth the show to me had brought.

For oft, when on my couch I lie,
In vacant or in pensive mood,
They flash upon that inward eye
Which is the bliss of solitude;
And then my heart with pleasure fills,
And dances with the daffodils.

WILLIAM WORDSWORTH

Rainy Song

Down the dripping pathway dancing through the rain,
Brown eyes of beauty, laugh to me again!

Eyes full of starlight, moist over fire,
Full of young wonder, touch my desire!

O like a brown bird, like a bird's flight,
Run through the rain drops lithely and light.

Body like a gypsy, like a wild queen,
Slim brown dress to slip through the green—

The little leaves hold you as soft as a child,
The little path loves you, the path that runs wild.

Who would not love you, seeing you move,
Warm-eyed and beautiful through the green grove?

Let the rain kiss you, trickle through your hair,
Laugh if my fingers mingle with it there,

Laugh if my cheek too is misty and drips—
Wetness is tender—laugh on my lips

The happy sweet laughter of love without pain,
Young love, the strong love, burning in the rain.

MAX EASTMAN

49

After Winter

He snuggles his fingers
In the blacker loam
The lean months are done with,
The fat to come.

His eyes are set
On a brushwood fire
But his heart is soaring
Higher and higher.

Though he stands ragged
An old scarecrow,
This is the way
His swift thoughts go,

"Butter beans fo' Clara
Sugar corn fo' Grace
An' fo' de little feller
Runnin' space.

"Radishes and lettuce
Eggplants and beets
Turnips fo' de winter
An' candied sweets.

"Homespun tobacco
Apples in de bin
Fo' smokin' an' fo' cider
When de folks draps in."

He thinks with the winter
His troubles are gone;
Ten acres unplanted
To raise dreams on.

The lean months are done with,
The fat to come.
His hopes, winter wanderers,
Hasten home.

"Butter beans fo' Clara
Sugar corn fo' Grace
An' fo' de little feller
Runnin' space. . . ."

STERLING BROWN

SPRING IN NEW HAMPSHIRE

(TO J. L. J. F. E.)

Too green the springing April grass,
   Too blue the silver-speckled sky,
For me to linger here, alas,
   While happy winds go laughing by,
Wasting the golden hours indoors,
Washing windows and scrubbing floors.

Too wonderful the April night,
   Too faintly sweet the first May flowers,
The stars too gloriously bright,
   For me to spend the evening hours,
When fields are fresh and streams are leaping,
Wearied, exhausted, dully sleeping.

CLAUDE MCKAY

SPRING GRASS

Spring grass, there is a dance to be danced for you.
Come up, spring grass, if only for young feet.
Come up, spring grass, young feet ask you.

Smell of the young spring grass,
You're a mascot riding on the wind horses.
You came to my nose and spiffed me. This is your
lucky year.

Young spring grass just after the winter,
Shoots of the big green whisper of the year,
Come up, if only for young feet.
Come up, young feet ask you.

CARL SANDBURG

RECONNAISSANCE

After the cloud embankments,
The lamentation of wind,
And the starry descent into time,
We came to the flashing waters and shaded our eyes
From the glare.

Alone with the shore and the harbor,
The stems of the cocoanut trees,
The fronds of silence and hushed music,
We cried for the new revelation
And waited for miracles to rise.

Where elements touch and merge,
Where shadows swoon like outcasts on the sand
And the tired moment waits, its courage gone—
There were we

In latitudes where storms are born.

ARNA BONTEMPS

My Heart Leaps Up When I Behold

My heart leaps up when I behold
  A rainbow in the sky:
So was it when my life began;
So is it now I am a man;
So be it when I shall grow old,
  Or let me die!
The Child is father of the Man;
And I could wish my days to be
Bound each to each by natural piety.

WILLIAM WORDSWORTH

The Unknown Color

I've often heard my mother say,
When great winds blew across the day,
And, cuddled close and out of sight,
The young pigs squealed with sudden fright
Like something speared or javelined,
"Poor little pigs, they see the wind."

COUNTEE CULLEN

Nothing Gold Can Stay

Nature's first green is gold,
Her hardest hue to hold.
Her early leaf's a flower;
But only so an hour.
Then leaf subsides to leaf.
So Eden sank to grief,
So dawn goes down to day.
Nothing gold can stay.

ROBERT FROST

The Sound
of Trees

THE SOUND OF TREES

I wonder about the trees.
Why do we wish to bear
Forever the noise of these
More than another noise
So close to our dwelling place?
We suffer them by the day
Till we lose all measure of pace,
And fixity in our joys,
And acquire a listening air.
They are that that talks of going
But never gets away;
And that talks no less for knowing,
As it grows wiser and older,
That now it means to stay.
My feet tug at the floor
And my head sways to my shoulder
Sometimes when I watch trees sway,
From the window or the door.
I shall set forth for somewhere,
I shall make the reckless choice
Some day when they are in voice
And tossing so as to scare
The white clouds over them on.
I shall have less to say,
But I shall be gone.

ROBERT FROST

58

Tree at My Window

Tree at my window, window tree,
My sash is lowered when night comes on;
But let there never be curtain drawn
Between you and me.

Vague dream-head lifted out of the ground,
And thing next most diffuse to cloud,
Not all your light tongues talking aloud
Could be profound.

But, tree, I have seen you taken and tossed,
And if you have seen me when I slept,
You have seen me when I was taken and swept
And all but lost.

That day she put our heads together,
Fate had her imagination about her,
Your head so much concerned with outer,
Mine with inner, weather.

ROBERT FROST

THE POPLAR

Why do you always stand there shivering
Between the white stream and the road?

The people pass through the dust
On bicycles, in carts, in motor cars;
The wagoners go by at dawn;
The lovers walk on the grass path at night.
Stir from your roots, walk, poplar!
You are more beautiful than they are.

I know that the white wind loves you,
Is always kissing you and turning up
The white lining of your green petticoat.
The sky darts through you like blue rain,
And the gray rain drips on your flanks
And loves you.
And I have seen the moon
Slip his silver penny into your pocket
As you straightened your hair;
And the white mist curling and hesitating
Like a bashful lover about your knees.

I know you, poplar;
I have watched you since I was ten.
But if you had a little real love,
A little strength,
You would leave your nonchalant idle lovers
And go walking down the white road
Behind the wagoners.

There are beautiful beeches down beyond the hill.
Will you always stand there shivering?

RICHARD ALDINGTON

LEAVES

One, two, and three,
Dead leaves drift from a tree.

Yesterday they loved
Wind and rain, the brush
Of wings
Soft and clean, that moved
Through them beyond the crush
Of things.
Yesterday they loved.

Yesterday they sang
Silver symphonies,
Raised high
Holy chants that rang
Leaf-wise through their trees;
As I,
Yesterday they sang.

Unremembered now,
They will soon lie warm
With snow;
They could grace a bough
Once, and love and charm,
Although
Unremembered now.

Trees so soon forget
Little leaves they had
Before,
Knowing spring will let
Them wake, vernal clad
With more;
Trees so soon forget.

Man dreams that he
Is more than a leaf on a tree.

COUNTEE CULLEN

CITY TREES

The trees along this city street,
  Save for the traffic and the trains,
Would make a sound as thin and sweet
  As trees in country lanes.

And people standing in their shade
  Out of a shower, undoubtedly
Would hear such music as is made
  Upon a country tree.

Oh, little leaves that are so dumb
  Against the shrieking city air,
I watch you when the wind has come—
  I know what sound is there.

EDNA ST. VINCENT MILLAY

Wild Plum

They are unholy who are born
   To love wild plum at night,
Who once have passed it on a road
   Glimmering and white.

It is as though the darkness had
   Speech of silver words,
Or as though a cloud of stars
   Perched like ghostly birds.

They are unpitied from their birth
   And homeless in men's sight
Who love, better than the earth,
   Wild plum at night.

ORRICK JOHNS

A TREE DESIGN

A tree is more than a shadow
blurred against the sky,
more than ink spilled on the fringe
of white clouds floating by.
A tree is more than an April design
or a blighted winter bough
where love and music used to be.
A tree is something in me,
very still and lonely now.

ARNA BONTEMPS

Bats, Loons, and
Other Creatures

THE BATS

In the June twilight, we looked without knowing why
At the peaked gable of a corner house;
And while we looked, a hundred bats flew out
From the patterned eaves over the beach and the lake;
And as soon as they had wavered high out of sight,
Came other hundreds at eight intervals:
Like black leaves dropping and gathered up again
In their own wind and blown to the setting sun.

After the firm birds of water and the bright birds of trees,
After the transparent golden air of day,
It is magical to see a host of shadows
Trembling upward over the mountaintop,
Or hovering past a balconied window at midnight
And flaking singly toward a mottled moon.
Even the bats are beautiful in Chapala
Where shadows leave the breast and fly away.

WITTER BYNNER

The Mountain and the Squirrel

The mountain and the squirrel
Had a quarrel,
And the former called the latter "Little prig;"
Bun replied,
"You are doubtless very big;
But all sorts of things and weather
Must be taken in together
To make up a year,
And a sphere.
And I think it no disgrace
To occupy my place.
If I'm not so large as you,
You are not so small as I,
And not half so spry.
I'll not deny you make
A very pretty squirrel track.
Talents differ; all is well and wisely put;
If I cannot carry forests on my back,
Neither can you crack a nut!"

RALPH WALDO EMERSON

The Fox and the Grapes

A Moral Tale for Those Who Fail

One summer's day a Fox was passing through
An orchard; faint he was and hungry, too.
When suddenly his keen eye chanced to fall
Upon a bunch of grapes above the wall.
"Ha! Just the thing!" he said. "Who could resist it!"
He eyed the purple cluster—jumped—and missed it.
"Ahem!" he coughed. "I'll take more careful aim,"
And sprang again. Results were much the same,
Although his leaps were desperate and high.
At length he paused to wipe a tearful eye,
And shrug a shoulder. "I am not so dry,
And lunch is bound to come within the hour . . .
Besides," he said, "I'm sure those grapes are sour."

THE MORAL IS: We somehow want the peach
That always dangles just beyond our reach;
Until we learn never to be upset
With what we find too difficult to get.

JOSEPH LAUREN

Four Little Foxes

Speak gently, Spring, and make no sudden sound;
For in my windy valley, yesterday I found
Newborn foxes squirming on the ground—
    Speak gently.

Walk gently, March; forbear the bitter blow;
Her feet within a trap, her blood upon the snow,
The four little foxes saw their mother go—
    Walk softly.

Go lightly, Spring; oh, give them no alarm;
When I covered them with boughs to shelter them
from harm,
The thin blue foxes suckled at my arm—
    Go lightly.

Step softly, March, with your rampant hurricane;
Nuzzling one another, and whimpering with pain,
The new little foxes are shivering in the rain—
    Step softly.

LEW SARETT

Twelfth Night: Song of the Camels

Not born to the forest are we,
Not born to the plain,
To the grass and the shadowing tree
And the splashing of rain.
Only the sand we know
And the cloudless sky.
The mirage and the deep-sunk well
And the stars on high.

To the sound of our bells we came
With huge soft stride,
Kings riding upon our backs,
Slaves at our side.
Out of the east drawn on
By a dream and a star,
Seeking the hills and the groves
Where the fixed towns are.

Our goal was no palace gate,
No temple of old,
But a child on his mother's lap
In the cloudy cold.
The olives were windy and white,
Dust swirled through the town,
As all in their royal robes
Our masters knelt down.

ELIZABETH COATSWORTH

72

THE BLIND MEN AND THE ELEPHANT

A HINDOO FABLE

It was six men of Indostan
   To learning much inclined,
Who went to see the Elephant
   (Though all of them were blind),
That each by observation
   Might satisfy his mind.

The *First* approached the Elephant,
   And happening to fall
Against his broad and sturdy side,
   At once began to bawl:
"God bless me! but the Elephant
   Is very like a wall!"

The *Second*, feeling of the tusk,
   Cried, "Ho! what have we here
So very round and smooth and sharp?
   To me 'tis mighty clear
This wonder of an Elephant
   Is very like a spear!"

The *Third* approached the animal,
   And happening to take
The squirming trunk within his hands,
   Thus boldly up and spake:
"I see," quoth he, "the Elephant
   Is very like a snake!"

The *Fourth* reached out an eager hand,
　　And felt about the knee.
"What most this wondrous beast is like
　　Is mighty plain," quoth he;
" 'Tis clear enough the Elephant
　　Is very like a tree!"

The *Fifth* who chanced to touch the ear,
　　Said: "E'en the blindest man
Can tell what this resembles most;
　　Deny the fact who can,
This marvel of an Elephant
　　Is very like a fan!"

The *Sixth* no sooner had begun
　　About the beast to grope,
Then, seizing on the swinging tail
　　That fell within his scope,
"I see," quoth he, "the Elephant
　　Is very like a rope!"

And so these men of Indostan
　　Disputed loud and long,
each in his own opinion
　　Exceeding stiff and strong,
Though each was partly in the right,
　　And all were in the wrong!

THE MORAL:
So oft in theologic wars,
    The disputants, I ween,
Rail on in utter ignorance
    Of what each other mean,
And prate about an Elephant
    Not one of them has seen!

JOHN GODFREY SAXE

The Loon

A lonely lake, a lonely shore,
A lone pine leaning on the moon;
All night the water-beating wings
Of a solitary loon.

With mournful wail from dusk to dawn
He gibbered at the taunting stars—
A hermit-soul gone raving mad,
And beating at his bars.

LEW SARETT

To a Winter Squirrel

That is the way God made you.
And what is wrong with it? Why, nothing.
Except that you are cold and cannot cook.

Merdice can cook. Merdice
of murdered heart and docked sarcastic soul,
Merdice
the bolted nomad, on a winter noon
cooks guts; and sits in gas.
(She has no shawl, her landlord has no coal.)

You out beyond the shellac of her look
and of her sill!
She envies you your furry
buffoonery
that enfolds your silver skill.
She thinks you are a mountain and a star, unbaffleable;
with sentient twitch and scurry.

GWENDOLYN BROOKS

Sea Fever

SEA BORN

My mother bore me in an island town,
So I love windy water and the sight
Of luggers sailing by in thin moonlight—
I wear the sea as others wear a crown!
My mother bore me near the spinning water,
Water was the first sound upon my ears,
And near the sea her mother bore her daughter,
Close to a window looking on the weirs.
Ever a wind is moaning where I go,
I never stand at night upon a quay,
But I must strain my eyes for sails that blow,
But I must strain my ears to hear the sea.
My mother bore me in a seaport town,
I wear the sea as others wear a crown!

So I have loved the sea as other men
Have loved the way of women who were dear;
Think it not strange that I should turn again
Back to the water and a windy pier.
For men turn back to women and so I,
Turn to the sea that I have loved the best,
Back to the waves and salty spume flung high,

Back to the furious beating of her breast.
So am I stifled now by streets and trees,
That have no space for breathing: I would wear
The splendid look of ships and breathe sea air.
Vessels and schooners, I am one with these.
My mother bore me in an island town—
I wear the sea as others wear a crown!

HAROLD VINAL

SAILOR

He sat upon the rolling deck
Half a world away from home,
And smoked a Capstan cigarette
And watched the blue waves tipped with foam.

He had a mermaid on his arm,
An anchor on his breast,
And tattooed on his back he had
A blue bird in a nest.

LANGSTON HUGHES

Sea Shell

Sea Shell, Sea Shell,
  Sing me a song, O please!
A song of ships, and sailormen,
  And parrots, and tropical trees,

Of islands lost in the Spanish Main
Which no man ever may find again,
Of fishes and corals under the waves,
And sea horses stabled in great green caves.

Sea Shell, Sea Shell,
Sing of the things you know so well.

AMY LOWELL

THE GOLDEN CITY OF ST. MARY

Out beyond the sunset, could I but find the way,
Is a sleepy blue laguna which widens to a bay,
And there's the Blessed City—so the sailors say—
   The Golden City of St. Mary.

It's built of fair marble—white—without a stain,
And in the cool twilight when the sea-winds wane
The bells chime faintly, like a soft, warm rain,
   In the Golden City of St. Mary.

Among the green palm trees where the fireflies shine,
Are the white tavern tables where the gallants dine,
Singing slow Spanish songs like old mulled wine,
   In the Golden City of St. Mary.

Oh I'll be shipping sunset-wards and westward-ho
Through the green toppling combers a-shattering
into snow,
Till I come to quiet moorings and a watch below,
   In the Golden City of St. Mary.

JOHN MASEFIELD

SKETCH

The shadows of the ships
Rock on the crest
In the low blue lustre
Of the tardy and the soft inrolling tide.

A long brown bar at the dip of the sky
Puts an arm of sand in the span of salt.

The lucid and endless wrinkles
Draw in, lapse and withdraw.
Wavelets crumble and white spent bubbles
Wash on the floor of the beach.

Rocking on the crest
In the low blue lustre
Are the shadows of the ships.

CARL SANDBURG

I Thought It Was Tangiers I Wanted

I know now
That Notre Dame is in Paris,
And the Seine is more to me now
Than a wriggling line on a map
Or a name in travel stories.

I know now
There is a Crystal Palace in Antwerp
Where a hundred women sell their naked bodies,
And the night-lovers of sailors
Wait for men on docks in Genoa.

I know now
That a great golden moon
Like a picture-book moon
Really rises behind palm groves
In Africa,
And the tom-toms do beat
In village squares under the mango trees.

I know now
That Venice is a church dome
And a network of canals,
Tangiers a whiteness under sun.

I thought
It was Tangiers I wanted,
Or the gargoyles of Notre Dame,
Or the Crystal Palace in Antwerp,
Or the golden palm-grove moon in Africa,
Or a church dome and a network of canals.

Happiness lives nowhere,
Some old fool said,
If not within oneself.

It's a sure thing
Notre Dame is in Paris,
But I thought it was Tangiers I wanted.

LANGSTON HUGHES

Trade Winds

In the harbour, in the island, in the Spanish Seas,
Are the tiny white houses and the orange trees,
And day-long, night-long, the cool and pleasant breeze
    Of the steady Trade Winds blowing.

There is the red wine, the nutty Spanish ale,
The shuffle of the dancers, the old salt's tale,
The squeaking fiddle, and the soughing in the sail
    Of the steady Trade Winds blowing.

And o' nights there's fireflies and the yellow moon,
And in the ghostly palm trees the sleepy tune
Of the quiet voice calling me, the long low croon
    Of the steady Trade Winds blowing.

JOHN MASEFIELD

Winners and Losers

Saturday's Child

Some are teethed on a silver spoon,
   With the stars strung for a rattle;
I cut my teeth as the black raccoon—
   For implements of battle.

Some are swaddled in silk and down,
   And heralded by a star;
They swathed my limbs in a sackcloth gown
   On a night that was black as tar.

For some, godfather and goddame
   The opulent fairies be;
Dame Poverty gave me my name,
   And Pain godfathered me.

For I was born on Saturday—
   "Bad time for planting a seed,"
Was all my father had to say,
   And, "One mouth more to feed."

Death cut the strings that gave me life,
   And handed me to Sorrow,
The only kind of middle wife
   My folks could beg or borrow.

COUNTEE CULLEN

Tangerines

In somewhat of a daze I lost the tangerines,
    and also the car;
but the car's loss seemed less important
than the bag of tangerines
I purchased on the sidewalk
    from a man who smiled
    behind the crates,
who smiled and took my coins
and filled the bag with tangerines
and something else of value vague
    but dear.

The street I searched in was all doors
    that rotted inward;
and one large room had rows of vacant beds;
another, naked mannikins with broken limbs;
a third had clutter gathered for the poor—
    but none my bag
    of orange tangerines
I purchased from a sidewalk saint
who vanished when the sale was made
and left me lost in smoggy mist
    and vaguely sad.

The streets are filled with cars;
someday I must look for mine.

ALEXANDER KARANIKAS

To James

Do you remember
How you won
That last race . . . ?
How you flung your body
At the start . . .
How your spikes
Ripped the cinders
In the stretch . . .
How you catapulted
Through the tape . . .
Do you remember . . . ?
Don't you think
I lurched with you
Out of those starting holes . . . ?
Don't you think
My sinews tightened
At those first
Few strides . . .
And when you flew into the stretch
Was not all my thrill
Of a thousand races
In your blood . . . ?
At your final drive
Through the finish line
Did not my shout
Tell of the
Triumphant ecstasy
Of victory . . . ?

Live
As I have taught you
To run, Boy—
It's a short dash
Dig your starting holes
Deep and firm
Lurch out of them
Into the straightaway
With all the power
That is in you
Look straight ahead
To the finish line
Think only of the goal
Run straight
Run high
Run hard
Save nothing
And finish
With an ecstatic burst
That carries you
Hurtling
Through the tape
To victory. . . .

FRANK HORNE

No Images

She does not know
Her beauty,
She thinks her brown body
Has no glory.

If she could dance
Naked,
Under palm trees
And see her image in the river
She would know.

But there are no palm trees
On the street,
And dishwater gives back no images.

WARING CUNEY

A Black Man Talks of Reaping

I have sown beside all waters in my day.
I planted deep, within my heart the fear
That wind or fowl would take the grain away.
I planted safe against this stark, lean year.

I scattered seed enough to plant the land
In rows from Canada to Mexico,
But for my reaping only what the hand
Can hold at once is all that I can show.

Yet what I sowed and what the orchard yields
My brother's sons are gathering stalk and root,
Small wonder then my children glean in fields
They have not sown, and feed on bitter fruit.

ARNA BONTEMPS

The Frogs Who Wanted a King

The frogs were living happy as could be
   In a wet marsh to which they all were suited;
From every sort of trouble they were free,
   And all night long they croaked, and honked, and
      hooted.
But one fine day a bullfrog said, "The thing
We never had and *must* have is a king."

So all the frogs immediately prayed;
   "Great Jove," they chorused from their swampy border,
"Send us a king and he will be obeyed,
   A king to bring a rule of Law and Order."
Jove heard and chuckled. That night in the bog
There fell a long and most impressive Log.

The swamp was silent; nothing breathed. At first
   The badly frightened frogs did never *once* stir;
But gradually some neared and even durst
   To touch, aye, even danced upon, the monster.
Whereat they croaked again, "Great Jove, oh hear!
Send us a *living* king, a king to fear."

Once more Jove smiled, and sent them down a Stork.
   "Long live—!" they croaked. But ere they framed the
      sentence,
The Stork bent down and, scorning knife or fork,
   Swallowed them all, with no time for repentance!

THE MORAL'S THIS: No matter what your lot,
It might be worse. Be glad with what you've got.

JOSEPH LAUREN

95

WHEN I WAS ONE-AND-TWENTY

When I was one-and-twenty
  I heard a wise man say,
"Give crowns and pounds and guineas
  But not your heart away;
Give pearls away and rubies
  But keep your fancy free."
But I was one-and-twenty,
  No use to talk to me.

When I was one-and-twenty
  I heard him say again,
"The heart out of the bosom
  Was never given in vain;
'Tis paid with sighs a-plenty
  And sold for endless rue."
And I am two-and-twenty,
  And oh, 'tis true, 'tis true.

A. E. HOUSMAN

The Winning of the TV West

When twilight comes to Prairie Street
On every TV channel,
The kids watch men with blazing guns
In jeans and checkered flannel.
Partner, the West is wild tonight—
There's going to be a battle
Between the sheriff's posse and
The gang that stole the cattle.
On every screen on Prairie Street
The sheriff roars his order:
"We've got to head those hombres off
Before they reach the border."
Clippoty-clop and bangity-bang
The lead flies left and right.
Paradise Valley is freed again
Until tomorrow night.
And all the kids on Prairie Street
Over and under ten
Can safely go to dinner now . . .
The West is won again.

JOHN T. ALEXANDER

Casey at the Bat

It looked extremely rocky for the Mudville nine that day,
The score stood four to six with but an inning left to play.
And so, when Cooney died at first, and Burrows did the
    same,
A pallor wreathed the features of the patrons of the game.
A straggling few got up to go, leaving there the rest,
With that hope which springs eternal within the human
    breast.
For they thought if only Casey could get a whack at that,
They'd put up even money with Casey at the bat.
But Flynn preceded Casey, and likewise so did Blake,
And the former was a pudding and the latter was a fake;
So on that stricken multitude a deathlike silence sat,
For there seemed but little chance of Casey's getting to
    the bat.
But Flynn let drive a single to the wonderment of all,
And the much despised Blakey tore the cover off the ball,
And when the dust had lifted and they saw what had
    occurred,
There was Blakey safe on second, and Flynn a-hugging
    third.
Then from the gladdened multitude went up a joyous yell,
It bounded from the mountaintop and rattled in the dell,
It struck upon the hillside, and rebounded on the flat,
For Casey, mighty Casey, was advancing to the bat.
There was ease in Casey's manner as he stepped into his
    place,
There was pride in Casey's bearing and a smile on Casey's
    face,

And when responding to the cheers he lightly doffed his
hat,
No stranger in the crowd could doubt, 'twas Casey at the
bat.
Ten thousand eyes were on him as he rubbed his hands
with dirt,
Five thousand tongues applauded as he wiped them on
his shirt;
And while the writhing pitcher ground the ball into his
hip—
Defiance gleamed from Casey's eye—a sneer curled
Casey's lip.
And now the leather-covered sphere came hurtling
through the air,
And Casey stood a-watching it in haughty grandeur there;
Close by the sturdy batsman the ball unheeded sped—
"That hain't my style," said Casey—"Strike one," the
Umpire said.
From the bleachers black with people there rose a sullen
roar,
Like the beating of the storm waves on a stern and distant
shore,
"Kill him! kill the Umpire!" shouted someone from the
stand—
And it's likely they'd have done it had not Casey raised
his hand.
With a smile of Christian charity great Casey's visage
shone,
He stilled the rising tumult and he bade the game go on;

He signaled to the pitcher and again the spheroid flew,
But Casey still ignored it and the Umpire said, "Strike
two."
"Fraud!" yelled the maddened thousands, and the echo
answered "Fraud."
But one scornful look from Casey and the audience was
awed;
They saw his face grow stern and cold; they saw his
muscles strain,
And they knew that Casey would not let that ball go by
again.
The sneer is gone from Casey's lip; his teeth are clenched
with hate,
He pounds with cruel violence his bat upon the plate;
And now the pitcher holds the ball, and now he lets it go,
And now the air is shattered by the force of Casey's blow.
Oh! somewhere in this favored land the sun is shining
bright,
The band is playing somewhere, and somewhere hearts
are light,
And somewhere men are laughing, and somewhere chil-
dren shout;
But there is no joy in Mudville—mighty Casey has Struck
Out.

ERNEST LAWRENCE THAYER

A Song in the Front Yard

I've stayed in the front yard all my life.
I want a peek at the back
Where it's rough and untended and hungry weed grows.
A girl gets sick of a rose.

I want to go in the back yard now
And maybe down the alley,
To where the charity children play.
I want a good time today.

They do some wonderful things.
They have some wonderful fun.
My mother sneers, but I say it's fine
How they don't have to go in at quarter to nine.
My mother, she tells me that Johnnie Mae
Will grow up to be a bad woman.
That George'll be taken to Jail soon or late
(On account of last winter he sold our back gate.)

But I say it's fine. Honest, I do.
And I'd like to be a bad woman, too,
And wear the brave stockings of night-black lace
And strut down the streets with paint on my face.

GWENDOLYN BROOKS

CONQUEST

My pathway lies through worse than death;
I meet the hours with bated breath.
My red blood boils, my pulses thrill,
I live life running up a hill.

Ah, no, I need no paltry play
Of makeshift tilts for holiday:
For I was born against the tide
And I must conquer that denied.

I shun no hardship, fear no foe;
The future calls and I must go:
I charge the line and dare the spheres
As I go fighting down the years.

GEORGIA DOUGLAS JOHNSON

WE WEAR THE MASK

We wear the mask that grins and lies,
It hides our cheeks and shades our eyes—
This debt we pay to human guile;
With torn and bleeding hearts we smile,
And mouth with myriad subtleties.

Why should the world be overwise,
In counting all our tears and sighs?
Nay, let them only see us, while
  We wear the mask.

We smile, but, O great Christ, our cries
To Thee from tortured souls arise.
We sing, but oh, the clay is vile
Beneath our feet, and long the mile;
But let the world dream otherwise,
  We wear the mask.

PAUL LAURENCE DUNBAR

JOHN HENRY

John Henry told his Captain,
"Well, a man ain't nothin' but a man,
And before I let that steam drill beat me down,
I'll die with a hammer in my hand,
I'll die with a hammer in my hand."

Well, the Captain says to John Henry,
"Gonna bring that steam drill around,
Gonna take that steam drill out on the job,
Gonna whop that steel on down,
Gonna whop that steel on down."

John Henry had a little woman,
And her name was Polly Ann,
When John Henry took sick and couldn't work one day,
Polly Ann drove steel like a man,
Polly Ann drove steel like a man.

John Henry said to his shaker,
"Shaker, why don't you sing?
I'm throwin' twelve pounds from my hips on down,
Just listen to that cold steel ring,
Just listen to that cold steel ring."

Well, the Captain says to John Henry,
"I believe this mountain's cavin' in."
John Henry said to the Captain,
" 'Tain't nothin' but my hammer suckin' wind,
'Tain't nothin' but my hammer suckin' wind."

The man that invented the steam drill
Thought that he was mighty fine;
John Henry made his fourteen feet,
While the steam drill it made only nine,
While the steam drill it made only nine.

John Henry, O John Henry,
Blood am runnin' red,
Falls right down his hammer to the ground,
Says, "I've beat him to the bottom but I'm dead."
Says, "I've beat him to the bottom but I'm dead."

John Henry had a little woman,
And the dress she wore was red,
She said, "I'm goin' down the railroad track,
I'm goin' where John Henry fell dead.
I'm goin' where John Henry fell dead."

They took John Henry to the buryin' ground,
And they buried him in the sand;
And every locomotive come roarin' round
Says, "There lies a steel-drivin' man."
Says, "There lies a steel-drivin' man."

ANONYMOUS

WE REAL COOL

THE POOL PLAYERS.
SEVEN AT THE GOLDEN SHOVEL.

We real cool. We
Left school. We

Lurk late. We
Strike straight. We

Sing sin. We
Thin gin. We

Jazz June. We
Die soon.

GWENDOLYN BROOKS

Youth

We have tomorrow
Bright before us
Like a flame.

Yesterday
A night-gone thing,
A sun-down name.

And dawn-today
Broad arch above the road we came.

We march!

LANGSTON HUGHES

Arithmetic is where numbers fly like pigeons in and out of your head.

Arithmetic tells you how many you lose or win if you know how many you had before you lost or won.

Arithmetic is seven eleven all good children go to heaven —or five six bundle of sticks.

Arithmetic is numbers you squeeze from your head to your hand to your pencil to your paper till you get the answer.

Arithmetic is where the answer is right and everything is nice and you can look out the window and see the blue sky—or the answer is wrong and you have to start all over and try again and see how it comes out this time.

If you take a number and double it and double it again and then double it a few more times, the number gets bigger and bigger and goes higher and higher and only arithmetic can tell you what the number is when you decide to quit doubling.

Arithmetic is where you have to multiply—and you carry the multiplication table in your head and hope you won't lose it.

If you have two animal crackers, one good and one bad, and you eat one and a striped zebra with streaks all over him eats the other, how many animal crackers will you have if somebody offers you five six seven and you say No no no and you say Nay nay nay and you say Nix nix nix?

If you ask your mother for one fried egg for breakfast and she gives you two fried eggs and you eat both of them, who is better in arithmetic, you or your mother?

CARL SANDBURG

KID STUFF

DECEMBER, 1942

The wise guys
tell me
that Christmas
is Kid Stuff . . .
Maybe they've got
something there—
Two thousand years ago
three wise guys
chased a star
across a continent
to bring
frankincense and myrrh
to a Kid
born in a manger
with an idea in his head . . .

And as the bombs
crash
all over the world
today
the real wise guys
know
that we've all
got to go chasing stars
again
in the hope
that we can get back
some of that
Kid Stuff
born two thousand years ago.

FRANK HORNE

How Do
I Love Thee?

How Do I Love Thee?

How do I love thee? Let me count the ways.
I love thee to the depth and breadth and height
My soul can reach, when feeling out of sight
For the ends of Being and ideal Grace.
I love thee to the level of everyday's
Most quiet need, by sun and candlelight.
I love thee freely, as men strive for Right;
I love thee purely, as they turn from Praise.
I love thee with the passion put to use
In my old griefs, and with my childhood's faith.
I love thee with a love I seemed to lose
With my lost saints—I love thee with the breath,
Smiles, tears, of all my life!—and, if God choose,
I shall but love thee better after death.

ELIZABETH BARRETT BROWNING

We'll Go No More A-Roving

So, we'll go no more a-roving
    So late into the night,
Though the heart be still as loving,
    And the moon be still as bright.

For the sword outwears its sheath,
    And the soul wears out the breast,
And the heart must pause to breathe,
    And love itself have rest.

Though the night was made for loving,
    And the day returns too soon,
Yet we'll go no more a-roving
    By the light of the moon.

BYRON, LORD GEORGE GORDON

A Red, Red Rose

O my luve is like a red, red rose,
  That's newly sprung in June.
O my luve is like the melodie
  That's sweetly played in tune.

As fair art thou, my bonnie lass,
  So deep in luve am I,
And I will luve thee still, my dear,
  Till a' the seas gang dry.

Till a' the seas gang dry, my dear,
  And the rocks melt wi' the sun!
And I will luve thee still, my dear,
  While the sands o' life shall run.

And fare thee weel, my only luve,
  And fare thee weel awhile!
And I will come again, my luve,
  Tho' it were ten thousand mile!

ROBERT BURNS

Song to Celia

Drink to me only with thine eyes,
    And I will pledge with mine;
Or leave a kiss but in the cup,
    And I'll not look for wine.
The thirst that from the soul doth rise
    Doth ask a drink divine;
But might I of Jove's nectar sup,
    I would not change for thine.

I sent thee late a rosy wreath,
    Not so much honoring thee
As giving it a hope, that there
    It could not withered be.
But thou thereon didst only breathe,
    And sent'st it back to me;
Since when it grows, and smells, I swear,
    Not of itself, but thee.

BEN JONSON

PATTERNS

I walk down the garden paths,
And all the daffodils
Are blowing, and the bright blue squills.
I walk down the patterned garden paths
In my stiff, brocaded gown.
With my powdered hair and jeweled fan,
I too am a rare
Pattern. As I wander down
The garden paths.
My dress is richly figured,
And the train
Makes a pink and silver strain
On the gravel, and the thrift
Of the borders.
Just a plate of current fashion,
Tripping by in high-heeled, ribboned shoes.
Not a softness anywhere about me,
Only whalebone and brocade.
And I sink on a seat in the shade
Of a lime tree. For my passion
Wars against the stiff brocade.
The daffodils and squills
Flutter in the breeze
As they please.
And I weep;
For the lime tree is in blossom
And one small flower has dropped upon my bosom.
And the plashing of waterdrops
In the marble fountain

Comes down the garden paths.
The dripping never stops.
Underneath my stiffened gown
Is the softness of a woman bathing in a marble basin,
A basin in the midst of hedges grown
So thick, she cannot see her lover hiding.
But she guesses he is near,
And the sliding of the water
Seems the stroking of a dear
Hand upon her.
What is Summer in a fine brocaded gown!
I should like to see it lying in a heap upon the ground.
All the pink and silver crumpled upon the ground.

I would be the pink and silver as I ran along the paths,
And he would stumble after,
Bewildered by my laughter.
I should see the sun flashing from his sword hilt and the
     buckles on his shoes.
I would choose
To lead him in a maze along the patterned paths,
A bright and laughing maze for my heavy-booted lover,
Till he caught me in the shade,
And the buttons of his waistcoat bruised my body as he
     clasped me,
Aching, melting, unafraid.
With the shadows of the leaves and the sundrops,
And the plopping of the waterdrops,
All about us in the open afternoon—

I am very like to swoon
With the weight of this brocade,
For the sun shifts through the shade.

Underneath the fallen blossom
In my bosom
Is a letter I have hid.
It was brought to me this morning by a rider from the
    Duke.
"Madam, we regret to inform you that Lord Hartwell
Died in action Thursday se'nnight."
As I read it in the white, morning sunlight,
The letters squirmed like snakes.
"Any answer, Madam," said my footman.
"No," I told him.
"See that the messenger takes some refreshment.
No, no answer."
And I walked into the garden,
Up and down the patterned paths,
In my stiff, correct brocade.
The blue and yellow flowers stood up proudly in the sun,
Each one.
I stood upright too,
Held rigid to the pattern
By the stiffness of my gown;
Up and down I walked,
Up and down.

In a month he would have been my husband.
In a month, here, underneath this lime,
We would have broken the pattern;

He for me, and I for him,
He as Colonel, I as Lady,
On this shady seat.
He had a whim
That sunlight carried blessing.
And I answered, "It shall be as you have said."
Now he is dead.
In Summer and in Winter I shall walk
Up and down
The patterned garden paths
In my stiff, brocaded gown.
The squills and daffodils
Will give place to pillared roses, and to asters, and to
    snow.
I shall go
Up and down
In my gown.
Gorgeously arrayed,
Boned and stayed.
And the softness of my body will be guarded from
    embrace
By each button, hook, and lace.
For the man who should loose me is dead,
Fighting with the Duke in Flanders,
In a pattern called a war.
Christ! What are patterns for?

AMY LOWELL

THE RIVER-MERCHANT'S WIFE

A LETTER

While my hair was still cut straight across my forehead
I played about the front gate, pulling flowers.
You came by on bamboo stilts, playing horse,
You walked about my seat, playing with blue plums.
And we went on living in the village of Chokan:
Two small people, without dislike or suspicion.

At fourteen I married My Lord you.
I never laughed, being bashful.
Lowering my head, I looked at the wall.
Called to, a thousand times, I never looked back.

At fifteen I stopped scowling,
I desired my dust to be mingled with yours
Forever and forever and forever.
Why should I climb the lookout?

At sixteen you departed,
You went into far Ku-to-yen, by the river of swirling
    eddies,
And you have been gone five months.
The monkeys make sorrowful noise overhead.
You dragged your feet when you went out.

By the gate now, the moss is grown, the different mosses,
Too deep to clear them away!
The leaves fall early this autumn, in wind.
The paired butterflies are already yellow with August
Over the grass in the West garden;
They hurt me. I grow older.
If you are coming down through the narrows of the river
    Kiang,
Please let me know beforehand,
And I will come out to meet you
    As far as Cho-fu-sa.

EZRA POUND

Sonnet CXXX

My mistress' eyes are nothing like the sun;
Coral is far more red than her lips' red:
If snow be white, why then her breasts are dun;
If hairs be wires, black wires grow on her head.
I have seen roses damask'd, red and white,
But no such roses see I in her cheeks;
And in some perfumes is there more delight
Than in the breath that from my mistress reeks.
I love to hear her speak, yet well I know
That music hath a far more pleasing sound:
I grant I never saw a goddess go,
My mistress, when she walks, treads on the ground:
    And yet, by heaven, I think my love as rare
    As any she belied with false compare.

WILLIAM SHAKESPEARE

Night Song at Amalfi

I asked the heaven of stars
   What I should give my love—
It answered me with silence,
   Silence above.

I asked the darkened sea
   Down where the fishermen go—
It answered me with silence,
   Silence below.

Oh, I could give him weeping,
   Or I could give him song—
But how can I give silence
   My whole life long?

SARA TEASDALE

The Look

Strephon kissed me in the spring,
    Robin in the fall,
But Colin only looked at me
    And never kissed at all.

Strephon's kiss was lost in jest,
    Robin's lost in play,
But the kiss in Colin's eyes
    Haunts me night and day.

SARA TEASDALE

Music, When Soft Voices Die

Music, when soft voices die,
Vibrates in the memory—
Odors, when sweet violets sicken,
Live within the sense they quicken.

Rose leaves, when the rose is dead,
Are heaped for the beloved's bed;
And so thy thoughts, when thou art gone,
Love itself shall slumber on.

PERCY BYSSHE SHELLEY

After August

Autumn Flight

You hear the din and drone of birds
in fiery maples banding like mad nomads;
shrieks of purple grackles hush the melody
of larks: the music of bright choristers
all eager for the southern skies.

You see white pollen softly floating
over bowers of brown asters,
dropping gently to the ground
with the diminuendo of the breeze.
The last red oak leaf spins
from its gray twig and rests
within its ripples on the pond.

You feel the turning of the wind
into the blizzard fury of the gale
that lashes into waves
the seas of barren forests.
The first starred snowflake falls
into the valley's lap a martyr,
melting to a tear upon the alien soil.
Avenging snowflakes sweep like gulls
in vertigoes of white and come
to rest in glistening victory.

ALEXANDER KARANIKAS

Autumn

The morns are meeker than they were,
    The nuts are getting brown;
The berry's cheek is plumper,
    The rose is out of town.

The maple wears a gayer scarf,
    The field a scarlet gown.
Lest I should be old-fashioned,
    I'll put a trinket on.

EMILY DICKINSON

Let It Be Forgotten

Let it be forgotten, as a flower is forgotten,
    Forgotten as a fire that once was singing gold,
Let it be forgotten for ever and ever,
    Time is a kind friend, he will make us old.

If anyone asks, say it was forgotten
    Long and long ago,
As a flower, as a fire, as a hushed footfall
    In a long forgotten snow.

SARA TEASDALE

THE GOLDEN TICKSEED

Now does the golden tickseed bloom its last;
The sweet alyssum, in their overthrow,
Breathe forth a final sweetness ere the blast
Of Autumn sounds and ere the firstling snow.
Now do the glad petunias, row on row,
Falter and fail, while to the ground they cast
Memorial petals—richly dying so.
The August days are done. Summer is past.

And I who love you, shall as quietly go
Out of your heart forever, whether we cry
"Not yet!" and whether we will it or no.
How else, then, shall another spring come by
Or other blooms attain the sun, and blow?
Summer is past. Even a rose must die.

GUSTAV DAVIDSON

THE REUNION

I loved the apple-sweetness of the air
And pines that settled slanting on the hill,
Indians old and soft with needles there,
Where once we stood, and both so strangely still.
We must have surely known what other days
Would come in other flaming autumn's flame.
And even though we walk through different ways
To different hills that hill remains the same.
Watch every splendor, envy all the sky,
But recognize the days we knew, and hear
The simple sounds we heard. As birds that fly
Southward to warmth, we shall come back one year.
The little teeth of time will make no mark
On any stone, on any leaf or bark.

OWEN DODSON

My November Guest

My Sorrow, when she's here with me,
   Thinks these dark days of autumn rain
Are beautiful as days can be;
She loves the bare, the withered tree;
   She walks the sodden pasture lane.

Her pleasure will not let me stay.
   She talks and I am fain to list:
She's glad the birds are gone away,
She's glad her simple worsted gray
   Is silver now with clinging mist.

The desolate deserted trees,
   The faded earth, the heavy sky,
The beauties she so truly sees,
She thinks I have no eye for these,
   And vexes me for reason why.

Not yesterday I learned to know
   The love of bare November days
Before the coming of the snow,
But it were vain to tell her so,
   And they are better for her praise.

ROBERT FROST

The House on the Hill

They are all gone away,
  The House is shut and still,
There is nothing more to say.

Through broken walls and gray
  The winds blow bleak and shrill:
They are all gone away.

Nor is there one today
  To speak them good or ill:
There is nothing more to say.

Why is it then we stray
  Around that sunken sill?
They are all gone away,

And our poor fancy-play
  For them is wasted skill:
There is nothing more to say.

There is ruin and decay
  In the House on the Hill:
They are all gone away,
There is nothing more to say.

E. A. ROBINSON

BANKING COAL

Whoever it was who brought the
    first wood and coal
To start the fire, did his part well;
Not all wood takes to fire from a match,
Nor coal from wood before it's burned to
    charcoal.
The wood and coal in question caught a
    flame
And flared up beautifully, touching the air
That takes a flame from anything.

Somehow the fire was furnaced,
And then the time was ripe for some to
    say,
"Right banking of the furnace saves the
    coal."
I've seen them set to work, each in his way,
Though all with shovels and with ashes,
Never resting till the fire seemed most
    dead;
Whereupon they'd crawl in hooded night-
    caps
Contentedly to bed. Sometimes the fire left
    alone
Would die, but like as not spiced tongues
Remaining by the hardest on till day would
    flicker up,
Never strong, to anyone who cared to rake
    for them.

But roaring fires never have been made
   that way.
I'd like to tell those folks that one grand
   flare
Transferred to memory tissues of the air
Is worth a life, or, for dull minds that
   turn in gold,
All money ever saved by banking coal.

JEAN TOOMER

THE DARK HILLS

Dark hills at evening in the west,
Where sunset hovers like a sound
Of golden horns that sang to rest
Old bones of warriors under ground,
Far now from all the bannered ways
Where flash the legions of the sun,
You fade—as if the last of days
Were fading, and all wars were done.

E. A. ROBINSON

The Last Leaf

I saw him once before,
As he passed by the door,
  And again
The pavement stones resound,
As he totters o'er the ground
  With his cane.

They say that in his prime,
Ere the pruning-knife of Time
  Cut him down,
Not a better man was found
By the Crier on his round
  Through the town.

But now he walks the streets,
And he looks at all he meets
  Sad and wan,
And he shakes his feeble head,
That it seems as if he said,
  "They are gone."

The mossy marbles rest
On the lips that he has prest
  In their bloom,
And the names he loved to hear
Have been carved for many a year
  On the tomb.

My grandmamma has said
Poor old lady, she is dead
   Long ago—
That he had a Roman nose,
And his cheek was like a rose
   In the snow;

But now his nose is thin,
And it rests upon his chin
   Like a staff,
And a crook is in his back,
And a melancholy crack
   In his laugh.

I know it is a sin
For me to sit and grin
   At him here;
But the old three-cornered hat,
And the breeches, and all that,
   Are so queer!

And if I should live to be
The last leaf upon the tree
   In the spring,
Let them smile, as I do now,
At the old forsaken bough
   Where I cling.

OLIVER WENDELL HOLMES

OVERTONES

I heard a bird at break of day
  Sing from the autumn trees
A song so mystical and calm,
  So full of certainties,
No man, I think, could listen long
  Except upon his knees.
Yet this was but a simple bird,
  Alone, among dead trees.

WILLIAM ALEXANDER PERCY

THE CRAZY WOMAN

I shall not sing a May song.
A May song should be gay.
I'll wait until November
And sing a song of gray.

I'll wait until November.
That is the time for me.
I'll go out in the frosty dark
And sing most terribly.

And all the little people
Will stare at me and say,
"That is the Crazy Woman
Who would not sing in May."

GWENDOLYN BROOKS

Strong Men

STRONG MEN

They dragged you from homeland,
They chained you in coffles,
They huddled you spoon-fashion in filthy hatches,
They sold you to give a few gentlemen ease.

They broke you in like oxen,
They scourged you,
They branded you,
They made your women breeders,
They swelled your numbers with bastards. . . .
They taught you the religion they disgraced.

You sang:
  Keep a inchin' along
  Lak a po' inch worm. . . .
You sang:
  Bye and bye
  I'm gonna lay down dis heaby load. . . .

You sang:
  Walk togedder, chillen,
  Dontcha git weary. . . .
    The strong men keep a-comin' on
    The strong men git stronger.

They point with pride to the roads you built for them,
They ride in comfort over the rails you laid for them.
They put hammers in your hands
And said—Drive so much before sundown.

You sang:
  Ain't no hammah
  In dis lan',
  Strikes lak mine, bebby,
  Strikes lak mine.

They cooped you in their kitchens,
They penned you in their factories,
They gave you the jobs that they were too good for,
They tried to guarantee happiness to themselves
By shunting dirt and misery to you.

You sang:
  Me an' muh baby gonna shine, shine
  Me an' muh baby gonna shine.
    The strong men keep a-comin' on
    The strong men git stronger . . .

They bought off some of your leaders
You stumbled, as blind men will . . .
They coaxed you, unwontedly soft voiced . . .
You followed a way.
Then laughed as usual.
They heard the laugh and wondered;
Uncomfortable;
Unadmitting a deeper terror. . . .
    The strong men keep a-comin' on
    Gittin' stronger. . . .

What, from the slums
Where they have hemmed you,
What, from the tiny huts
They could not keep from you—
What reaches them
Making them ill at ease, fearful?
Today they shout prohibition at you
"Thou shalt not this"
"Thou shalt not that"
"Reserved for whites only"
You laugh.

One thing they cannot prohibit—
    The strong men . . . coming on
    The strong men gittin' stronger.
    Strong men . . .
    Stronger . . .

STERLING A. BROWN

Not in Vain

If I can stop one heart from breaking,
I shall not live in vain:
If I can ease one life the aching,
Or cool one pain,
Or help one fainting robin
Unto his nest again,
I shall not live in vain.

EMILY DICKINSON

EPITAPHS:
FOR PAUL LAURENCE DUNBAR

Born of the sorrowful of heart,
   Mirth was a crown upon his head;
Pride kept his twisted lips apart
   In jest, to hide a heart that bled.

COUNTEE CULLEN

MERCY

FROM THE MERCHANT OF VENICE

The quality of mercy is not strained;
It droppeth as the gentle rain from heaven
Upon the place beneath: it is twice blest—
It blesseth him that gives and him that takes:
'Tis mightiest in the mightiest; it becomes
The throned monarch better than his crown:
His sceptre shows the force of temporal power,
The attribute to awe and majesty,
Wherein doth sit the dread and fear of kings;
But mercy is above this sceptred sway—
It is enthroned in the hearts of kings,
It is an attribute to God himself;
And earthly power doth then show likest God's,
When mercy seasons justice.

WILLIAM SHAKESPEARE

A Man's a Man For a' That

Is there, for honest poverty,
That hings his head, an' a' that?
The coward slave, we pass him by,
We dare be poor for a' that!
For a' that, an' a' that,
Our toils obscure, an' a' that;
The rank is but the guinea's stamp;
The man's the gowd[1] for a' that.

What though on hamely fare we dine,
Wear hodden-gray,[2] an' a' that;
Gie fools their silks, and knaves their wine,
A man's a man for a' that.
For a' that, an' a' that,
Their tinsel show, an' a' that;
The honest man, tho' e'er sae poor,
Is king o' men for a' that.

Ye see yon birkie,[3] ca'd a lord,
Wha struts, an' stares, an' a' that;
Tho' hundreds worship at his word,
He's but a cuif[4] for a' that:
For a' that, an' a' that,
His riband, star, an' a' that,
The man o' independent mind,
He looks and laughs at a' that.

A prince can mak a belted knight,
A marquis, duke, an' a' that;
But an honest man's aboon[5] his might,
Guid faith, he mauna fa[6] that!
For a' that, an' a' that,
Their dignities, an' a' that,
The pith o' sense, an' pride o' worth,
Are higher rank than a' that.

Then let us pray that come it may
(As come it will for a' that)
That Sense and Worth o'er a' the earth,
May bear the gree[7] and a' that!
For a' that, and a' that,
It's coming yet, for a' that,
That man to man the world o'er
Shall brothers be for a' that.

ROBERT BURNS

---

[1] gold   [2] homespun   [3] young chap   [4] fool
[5] above   [6] try   [7] prize

THE MAN WITH THE HOE

GOD MADE MAN IN HIS OWN IMAGE,
IN THE IMAGE OF GOD MADE HE HIM.—GENESIS.

Bowed by the weight of centuries he leans
Upon his hoe and gazes on the ground,
The emptiness of ages in his face,
And on his back the burden of the world.
Who made him dead to rapture and despair,
A thing that grieves not and that never hopes,
Stolid and stunned, a brother to the ox?
Who loosened and let down this brutal jaw?
Whose was the hand that slanted back this brow?
Whose breath blew out the light within this brain?

Is this the Thing the Lord God made and gave
To have dominion over sea and land;
To trace the stars and search the heavens for power;
To feel the passion of Eternity?
Is this the dream He dreamed who shaped the suns
And marked their ways upon the ancient deep?
Down all the caverns of Hell to their last gulf
There is no shape more terrible than this—
More tongued with censure of the world's blind greed—
More filled with signs and portents for the soul—
More packed with danger to the universe.

What gulfs between him and the seraphim!
Slave of the wheel of labor, what to him
Are Plato and the swing of Pleiades?

144

What the long reaches of the peaks of song,
The rift of dawn, the reddening of the rose?
Thru this dread shape the suffering ages look;
Time's tragedy is in that aching stoop;
Thru this dread shape humanity betrayed,
Plundered, profaned and disinherited,
Cries protest to the Judges of the World,
A protest that is also prophecy.

O masters, lords and rulers in all lands,
Is this the handiwork you give to God,
This monstrous thing distorted and soul-quenched?
How will you ever straighten up this shape;
Touch it again with immortality;
Give back the upward looking and the light;
Rebuild in it the music and the dream;
Make right the immemorial infamies,
Perfidious wrongs, immedicable woes?

O masters, lords and rulers in all lands,
How will the future reckon with this Man?
How answer his brute question in that hour
When whirlwinds of rebellion shake all shores?
How will it be with kingdoms and with kings—
With those who shaped him to the thing he is—
When this dumb Terror shall rise to judge the world,
After the silence of the centuries?

EDWIN MARKHAM

FISHERMEN

When three, he fished these lakes,
Curled sleeping on a lip of rock,
Crib blankets tucked from ants and fishbone flies,
Twitching as the strike of bass and snarling reel
Uncoiled my shouts not quit
Till he jerked blinking up on all-fours,
Swaying with the winking leaves.
Strong awake, he shook his cane pole like a spoon
And dipped among the wagging perch
Till, tired, he drew his silver rubber blade
And poked the winding fins that tugged our string,
Or sprayed the dimpling minnows with his plastic gun,
Or, rainstruck, squirmed to my armpit on the poncho.

Ten years uncurled him, thinned him hard.
Now, far he casts his line into the wrinkled blue
And easy toes a rock, reel on his thigh
Till bone and crank cry out the strike
He takes with manchild chuckles, cunning
In his play of zigzag line and plunging silver.

Now fishing far from me, he strides through rain,
    shoulders
A spiny ridge of pines, and disappears
Near lakes that cannot be, while I must choose
To go or stay: bring blanket, blade, and gun,
Or stand a fisherman.

JAMES A. EMANUEL

Now That He Is Safely Dead

Now that he is safely dead
let us praise him
        build monuments to his glory
    sing hosannas to his name.

Dead men make
such convenient heroes: They
        cannot rise
    to challenge the images
        we would fashion from their lives.

And besides,
it is easier to build monuments
    than to make a better world.

So, now that he is safely dead
we, with eased consciences
        will teach our children
    that he was a great man . . . knowing

that the cause for which he lived
is still a cause
    and the dream for which he died
        is still a dream,
    —a dead man's dream.

CARL W. HINES, JR.

ABRAHAM LINCOLN WALKS AT MIDNIGHT

It is portentous, and a thing of state
   That here at midnight, in our little town
A mourning figure walks, and will not rest
   Near the old courthouse pacing up and down,

Or by his homestead, or the shadowed yards
   He lingers where his children used to play,
Or through the market, on the well-worn stones
   He stalks until the dawn-stars burn away.

A bronzed, lank man! His suit of ancient black,
   A famous high-top-hat and plain worn shawl
Make him the quaint great figure that men love,
   The prairie-lawyer, master of us all.

He cannot sleep upon his hillside now.
   He is among us, as in times before!
And we who toss and lie awake for long
   Breathe deep, and start, to see him pass the door.

His head is bowed. He thinks on men and kings.
   Yea, when the sick world cries, how can he sleep?
Too many peasants fight, they know not why,
   Too many homesteads in black terror weep.

The sins of all the war lords burn his heart.
   He sees the dreadnaughts scouring every main.
He carries on his shawl-wrapt shoulders now
   The bitterness, the folly and the pain.

He cannot rest until a spirit-dawn
   Shall come—the shining hope of Europe free;
The league of sober folk, the Workers' Earth
   Bringing long peace to Cornland, Alp, and Sea.

It breaks his heart that kings must murder still,
   That all his hours of travail here for men
Seem yet in vain. And who will bring white peace
   That he may sleep upon his hill again?

VACHEL LINDSAY

Stanley Meets Mutesa

Such a time of it they had;
The heat of the day
The chill of the night
And the mosquitoes that followed.
Such was the time and
They bound for a kingdom.

The thin weary line of carriers
With tattered dirty rags to cover their backs;
The battered bulky chests
That kept on falling off their shaven heads.
Their tempers high and hot
The sun fierce and scorching
With it rose their spirits
With its fall their hopes
As each day sweated their bodies dry and
Flies clung in clumps on their sweat scented backs.
Such was the march
And the hot season just breaking.

Each day a weary pony dropped,
Left for the vultures on the plains;
Each afternoon a human skeleton collapsed,
Left for the Masai on the plains;
But the march trudged on
Its khaki leader in front
He the spirit that inspired.
He the light of hope.

Then came the afternoon of a hungry march,
A hot and hungry march it was;
The Nile and the Nyanza
Lay like two twins
Azure across the green countryside.
The march leapt on chaunting
Like young gazelles to a water hole.
Hearts beat faster
Loads felt lighter
As the cool water lapt their sore feet.
No more the dread of hungry hyenas
But only tales of valour when
At Mutesa's court fires are lit.
No more the burning heat of the day
But song, laughter and dance.

The village looks on behind banana groves,
Children peer behind reed fences.
Such was the welcome
No singing women to chaunt a welcome
Or drums to greet the white ambassador;
Only a few silent nods from aged faces
And one rumbling drum roll
To summon Mutesa's court to parley
For the country was not sure.

The gate of reeds is flung open,
There is silence
But only a moment's silence—
A silence of assessment.
The tall black king steps forward,
He towers over the thin bearded white man,
Then grabbing his lean white hand
Manages to whisper
"Mtu mweupe karibu"
White man you are welcome.
The gate of polished reed closes behind them
And the West is let in.

JAMES D. RUBADIRI

The Poet
and His Song

The Poet and His Song

A song is but a little thing,
And yet what joy it is to sing!
In hours of toil it gives me zest,
And when at eve I long for rest;
When cows come home along the bars,
   And in the fold I hear the bell,
As Night, the shepherd, herds his stars,
   I sing my song, and all is well.

There are no ears to hear my lays,
No lips to lift a word of praise;
But still, with faith unfaltering,
I live and laugh and love and sing.
What matters yon unheeding throng?
   They cannot feel my spirit's spell,
Since life is sweet and love is long,
   I sing my song, and all is well.

My days are never days of ease;
I till my ground and prune my trees.
When ripened gold is all the plain,
I put my sickle to the grain.
I labor hard, and toil and sweat,
   While others dream within the dell;
But even while my brow is wet,
   I sing my song, and all is well.

Sometimes the sun, unkindly hot,
My garden makes a desert spot;
Sometimes a blight upon the tree
Takes all my fruit away from me;
And then with throes of bitter pain
Rebellious passions rise and swell;
But—life is more than fruit or grain,
And so I sing, and all is well.

PAUL LAURENCE DUNBAR

RHAPSODY

I am glad daylong for the gift of song,
  For time and change and sorrow;
For the sunset wings and the world-end things
  Which hang on the edge of tomorrow.
I am glad for my heart whose gates apart
  Are the entrance-place of wonders,
Where dreams come in from the rush and din
  Like sheep from the rains and thunders.

WILLIAM STANLEY BRAITHWAITE

REQUIEM

Under the wide and starry sky
Dig the grave and let me lie:
Glad did I live and gladly die,
And I laid me down with a will.

This be the verse you grave for me:
Here he lies where he long'd to be;
Home is the sailor, home from the sea,
And the hunter home from the hill.

ROBERT LOUIS STEVENSON

O Daedalus, Fly Away Home

Drifting night in the Georgia pines,
coonskin drum and jubilee banjo.
   Pretty Malinda, dance with me.

Night is juba, night is conjo.
   Pretty Malinda, dance with me.

Night is an African juju man
weaving a wish and a weariness together
   to make two wings.

   O fly away home fly away

Do you remember Africa?

   O cleave the air fly away home

My gran, he flew back to Africa,
just spread his arms and
   flew away home.

Drifting night in the windy pines;
night is a laughing, night is a longing.
   Pretty Malinda, come to me.

Night is a mourning juju man
weaving a wish and a weariness together
to make two wings.

O fly away home fly away

ROBERT HAYDEN

A Song

Thou art the soul of a summer's day,
Thou art the breath of the rose.
  But the summer is fled
  And the rose is dead.
Where are they gone, who knows, who knows?

Thou art the blood of my heart o' hearts,
Thou art my soul's repose,
  But my heart grows numb
  And my soul is dumb.
Where art thou, love, who knows, who knows?

Thou art the hope of my after years—
Sun for my winter snows.
  But the years go by
  'Neath a clouded sky.
Where shall we meet, who knows, who knows?

PAUL LAURENCE DUNBAR

SMELLS

Why is it that the poets tell
So little of the sense of smell?
These are the odors I love well:

The smell of coffee freshly ground;
Of rich plum pudding, holly-crowned;
Or onions fried and deeply browned.

The fragrance of a fumy pipe;
The smell of apples, newly ripe;
And printer's ink on leaden type.

Woods by moonlight in September
Breathe most sweet; and I remember
Many a smoky campfire ember.
Camphor, turpentine, and tea,
The balsam of a Christmas tree,
These are whiffs of gramarye . . .
A *ship smells best of all to me!*

CHRISTOPHER MORLEY

THE BELLS

I

Hear the sledges with the bells—
  Silver bells!
What a world of merriment their melody foretells!
  How they tinkle, tinkle, tinkle,
    In the icy air of night!
  While the stars that oversprinkle
  All the heavens, seem to twinkle
    With a crystalline delight;
  Keeping time, time, time,
  In a sort of Runic rhyme,
To the tintinnabulation that so musically wells
  From the bells, bells, bells, bells,
    Bells, bells, bells—
From the jingling and the tinkling of the bells.

II

Hear the mellow wedding bells—
  Golden bells!
What a world of happiness their harmony foretells!
  Through the balmy air of night
  How they ring out their delight!—
    From the molten-golden notes,
    And all in tune,
  What a liquid ditty floats
To the turtledove that listens, while she gloats
    On the moon!
  Oh, from out the sounding cells,
What a gush of euphony voluminously wells!

How it swells!
How it dwells
On the Future!—how it tells
Of the rapture that impels
To the swinging and the ringing
Of the bells, bells, bells—
Of the bells, bells, bells, bells,
Bells, bells, bells—
To the rhyming and the chiming of the bells!

III
Hear the loud alarum bells—
Brazen bells!
What a tale of terror, now their turbulency tells!
In the startled ear of night
How they scream out their affright!
Too much horrified to speak,
They can only shriek, shriek,
Out of tune,
In a clamorous appealing to the mercy of the fire,
In a mad expostulation with the deaf and frantic fire,
Leaping higher, higher, higher,
With a desperate desire,
And a resolute endeavor
Now—now to sit, or never,
By the side of the pale-faced moon.
Oh, the bells, bells, bells!
What a tale their terror tells
Of Despair!
How they clang, and clash, and roar!
What a horror they outpour

On the bosom of the palpitating air!
    Yet the ear, it fully knows,
        By the twanging,
        And the clanging,
    How the danger ebbs and flows;
    Yet the ear distinctly tells,
        In the jangling,
        And the wrangling,
    How the danger sinks and swells,
By the sinking or the swelling in the anger of the bells—
        Of the bells—
    Of the bells, bells, bells, bells,
        Bells, bells, bells—
In the clamor and the clanging of the bells!

IV
Hear the tolling of the bells—
    Iron bells!
What a world of solemn thought their monody compels!
    In the silence of the night,
    How we shiver with affright
At the melancholy menace of their tone!
    For every sound that floats
    From the rust within their throats
        Is a groan.
And the people—ah, the people—
They that dwell up in the steeple,
        All alone,
    And who, tolling, tolling, tolling,
        In that muffled monotone,
    Feel a glory in so rolling

On the human heart a stone—
They are neither man nor woman—
They are neither brute nor human—
They are Ghouls:—
And their king it is who tolls:—
and he rolls, rolls, rolls,
Rolls
A pæan from the bells!
And his merry bosom swells
With the pæan of the bells!
And he dances, and he yells;
Keeping time, time, time,
In a sort of Runic rhyme,
To the pæan of the bells:—
Of the bells:
Keeping time, time, time,
In a sort of Runic rhyme,
To the throbbing of the bells—
Of the bells, bells, bells—
To the sobbing of the bells:—
Keeping time, time, time,
As he knells, knells, knells,
In a happy Runic rhyme,
To the rolling of the bells—
Of the bells, bells, bells:—
To the tolling of the bells—
Of the bells, bells, bells, bells,
Bells, bells, bells—
To the moaning and the groaning of the bells.

EDGAR ALLAN POE

The Jazz of This Hotel

Why do I curse the jazz of this hotel?
I like the slower toms-toms of the sea;
I like the slower toms-toms of the thunder;
I like the more deliberate dancing knee
Of outdoor love, of outdoor talk and wonder.
I like the slower deeper violin
Of the wind across the fields of Indian corn;
I like the far more ancient violoncello
Of whittling loafers telling stories mellow
Down at the village grocery in the sun;
I like the slower bells that ring for church
Across the Indiana landscape old.
Therefore I curse the jazz of this hotel
That seems so hot, but is so hard and cold.

VACHEL LINDSAY

The Tropics in New York

Bananas ripe and green, and gingerroot,
  Cocoa in pods and alligator pears,
And tangerines and mangoes and grapefruit,
  Fit for the highest prize at parish fairs,

Set in the window, bringing memories
  Of fruittrees laden by low-singing rills,
And dewy dawns, and mystical blue skies
  In benediction over nun-like hills.

My eyes grew dim, and I could no more gaze;
  A wave of longing through my body swept,
And, hungry for the old, familiar ways,
  I turned aside and bowed my head and wept.

CLAUDE MCKAY

ARS POETICA

A poem should be palpable and mute
As a globed fruit

Dumb
As old medallions to the thumb

Silent as the sleeve-worn stone
Of casement ledges where the moss has grown—

A poem should be wordless
As the flight of birds

A poem should be motionless in time
As the moon climbs

Leaving, as the moon releases
Twig by twig the night-entangled trees,

Leaving, as the moon behind the winter leaves,
Memory by memory the mind—

A poem should be motionless in time
As the moon climbs

A poem should be equal to:
Not true

For all the history of grief
An empty doorway and a maple leaf

For love
The leaning grasses and two lights above the sea—

A poem should not mean
But be.

ARCHIBALD MACLEISH

Your World

Your world is as big as you make it.
I know, for I used to abide
In the narrowest nest in a corner,
My wings pressing close to my side.

But I sighted the distant horizon
Where the skyline encircled the sea
And I throbbed with a burning desire
To travel this immensity.

I battered the cordons around me
And cradled my wings on the breeze
Then soared to the uttermost reaches
With rapture, with power, with ease!

GEORGIA DOUGLAS JOHNSON

Literary Love

I broke my heart because of you, my dear;
I wept full many an unmanly tear—
But as in agony I lay awake
I thought, "What lovely poems this will make!"

HARRY KEMP

Nothing Happens
Only Once

CIRCLE ONE

FOR GORDON HEATH

Nothing happens only once,
Nothing happens only here,
Every love that lies asleep
Wakes today another year.

Why we sailed and how we prosper
Will be sung and lived again;
All the lands repeat themselves,
Shore for shore and men for men.

OWEN DODSON

ANTHEM FOR DOOMED YOUTH

What passing-bells for these who die as cattle?
Only the monstrous anger of the guns.
Only the stuttering rifles' rapid rattle
Can patter out their hasty orisons.
No mockeries for them from prayers or bells,
Nor any voice of mourning save the choirs—
The shrill, demented choirs of wailing shells;
And bugles calling for them from sad shires.
What candles may be held to speed them all?
Not in the hands of boys, but in their eyes
Shall shine the holy glimmers of good-byes.
The pallor of girls' brows shall be their pall;
Their flowers the tenderness of silent minds,
And each slow dusk a drawing-down of blinds.

WILFRED OWEN

BALLADE BY THE FIRE

Slowly I smoke and hug my knee,
　The while a witless masquerade
Of things that only children see
　Floats in a mist of light and shade:
　They pass, a flimsy cavalcade,
And with a weak, remindful glow,
　The falling embers break and fade,
As one by one the phantoms go.

Then, with a melancholy glee
　To think where once my fancy strayed,
I muse on what the years may be
　Whose coming tales are all unsaid,
　Till tongs and shovel, snugly laid
Within their shadowed niches, grow
　By grim degrees to pick and spade,
As one by one the phantoms go.

But then, what though the mystic Three
　Around me ply their merry trade?—
And Charon soon may carry me
　Across the gloomy Stygian glade?—
　Be up, my soul! nor be afraid
Of what some unborn year may show;
　But mind your human debts are paid,
As one by one the phantoms go.

ENVOY

Life is the game that must be played:
  This truth at least, good friend, we know;
So live and laugh, nor be dismayed
  As one by one the phantoms go.

E. A. ROBINSON

The Debt

This is the debt I pay
Just for one riotous day,
Years of regret and grief,
Sorrow without relief.

Pay it I will to the end—
Until the grave, my friend,
Gives me a true release—
Gives me the clasp of peace.

Slight was the thing I bought,
Small was the debt I thought,
Poor was the loan at best—
God! but the interest!

PAUL LAURENCE DUNBAR

MOTHER TO SON

Well, son, I'll tell you:
Life for me ain't been no crystal stair.
It's had tacks in it,
And splinters,
And boards torn up,
And places with no carpet on the floor—
Bare.
But all the time
I'se been a-climbin' on,
And reachin' landin's,
And turnin' corners,
And sometimes goin' in the dark
Where there ain't been no light.
So, boy, don't you turn back.
Don't you set down on the steps
'Cause you finds it kinder hard.
Don't you fall now—
For I'se still goin', honey,
I'se still climbin',
And life for me ain't been no crystal stair.

LANGSTON HUGHES

THE TREEHOUSE

To every man
His treehouse,
A green splice in the humping years,
Spartan with narrow cot
And prickly door.

To every man
His twilight flash
Of luminous recall

    of tiptoe years
    in leaf-strung flight;
    of days of squirm and bite
    that waved antennas through the grass
    of nights
    when every moving thing
    was girlshaped,
    expectantly turning.

To every man
His house below
And his house above—
With perilous stairs
Between.

JAMES A. EMANUEL

Dirge: from Cymbeline

Fear no more the heat o' th' sun,
   Nor the furious winter's rages,
Thou thy worldy task hast done,
   Home art gone and ta'en thy wages.
Golden lads and girls all must,
As chimney sweepers, come to dust.

Fear no more the frown o' th' great,
   Thou art past the tyrant's stroke,
Care no more to clothe and eat,
   To thee the reed is as the oak:
The sceptre, learning, physic, must
All follow this and come to dust.

Fear no more the lightning-flash.
   Nor th' all-dreaded thunderstone.
Fear not slander, censure rash.
   Thou hast finish'd joy and moan.
All lovers young, all lovers must
Consign to thee and come to dust.

No exorcisor harm thee!
Nor no witchcraft charm thee!
Ghost unlaid forbear thee!
Nothing ill come near thee!
Quiet consummation have,
And renowned be thy grave!

WILLIAM SHAKESPEARE

AUTHOR INDEX

Aldington, Richard 60
Alexander, John T. 97
Anonymous 104
Austin, Mary 34
Bontemps, Arna 54, 66, 93
Braithwaite, William Stanley 156
Brooks, Gwendolyn 76, 101, 106, 136
Brown, Sterling 50, 138
Browning, Elizabeth Barrett 112
Burns, Robert 114, 142
Bynner, Witter 68
Byron, Lord George Gordon 113
Coatsworth, Elizabeth 72
Cullen, Countee 32, 47, 55, 62, 88, 141
Cuney, Waring 92
Davidson, Gustav 128
Davis, F. Marshall 37
Dickinson, Emily 21, 127, 140
Dodson, Owen 129, 172
Dunbar, Paul Laurence 103, 154, 160, 176
Eastman, Max 49
Emanuel, James A. 24, 146, 178
Emerson, Ralph Waldo 69
Frost, Robert 21, 56, 58, 59, 130
Hayden, Robert 158
Hines, Carl W. Jr. 147
Holmes, Oliver Wendell 134
Horne, Frank 90, 109
Housman, A.E. 96
Hughes, Langston 19, 29, 44, 80, 84, 107, 177
Johns, Orrick 65
Johnson, Georgia Douglas 20, 102, 170
Johnson, James Weldon 41
Jonson, Ben 115
Karanikas, Alexander 89, 126

Keats, John 22
Kemp, Harry 170
Lauren, Joseph 70, 94
Lazarus, Emma 35
Lindsay, Vachel 148, 166
Lowell, Amy 81, 116
McKay, Claude 30, 40, 52, 167
MacLeish, Archibald 168
Markham, Edwin 144
Masefield, John 82, 86
Millay, Edna St. Vincent 43, 64
Monroe, Harriet 20
Morley, Christopher 161
Owen, Wilfred 173
Percy, William Alexander 136
Poe, Edgar Allan 162
Pound, Ezra 120
Robinson, E.A. 131, 133, 174
Roethke, Theodore 36
Rubadiri, James D. 150
Sandburg, Carl 53, 83, 108
Sarett, Lew 71, 75
Saxe, John Godfrey 73
Shakespeare, William 122, 141, 179
Shapiro, Karl 42
Shelley, Percy Bysshe 124
Stevenson, Robert Louis 26, 157
Tagore, Rabindranath 28
Teasdale, Sara 123, 124, 127
Thayer, Ernest Lawrence 98
Toomer, Jean 132
Van Doren, Carl 46
Vinal, Harold 78
Wordsworth, William 48, 55

TITLE INDEX

Abraham Lincoln Walks at Midnight 148
After Winter 50
America 40
Anthem for Doomed Youth 173
Arithmetic 108
Ars Poetica 168
Autumn 127
Autumn Flight 126
Ballade by the Fire 174
Banking Coal 132
Bats, The 68
Bells, The 162
Black Man Talks of Reaping, A 93
Blind Men and the Elephant, The 73
Blue Ridge, The 20
Casey at the Bat 98
Circle One 172
City Trees 64
Conquest 102
Crazy Woman, The 136
Dark Hills, The 133
Debt, The 176
Dirge 179
Dreams 19
Epitaphs: For Paul Laurence Dunbar 141
Fishermen 146
Four Little Foxes 71
Fox and the Grapes, The 70
Frogs Who Wanted a King, The 94
Golden City of St. Mary, The 82
Golden Tickseed, The 128
Grass on the Mountain, The 34
Hands of a Brown Woman 37
House on the Hill, The 131
How Do I Love Thee? 112

I Dream a World	29
I Thought It Was Tangiers I Wanted	84
I Wandered Lonely as a Cloud	48
If You Should Go	32
Jazz of This Hotel, The	166
John Henry	104
Kid Stuff	109
La Belle Dame Sans Merci	22
Last Leaf, The	134
Leaves	62
Let It Be Forgotten	127
Literary Love	170
Look, The	124
Loon, The	75
Man with the Hoe, The	144
Man's a Man for A' That, A	142
Manhole Covers	42
Mercy	141
Mother to Son	177
Mountain and the Squirrel, The	69
Music, When Soft Voices Die	124
My City	41
My Heart Leaps Up When I Behold	55
My November Guest	130
New Colossus, The	35
Night Journey	36
Night Song at Amalfi	123
No Images	92
Not in Vain	140
Nothing Gold Can Stay	56
Now That He Is Safely Dead	147
O Daedalus, Fly Away Home	158
Overtones	136
Paper Boats	28
Patterns	116

Peck of Gold, A   21
Poet and His Song, The   154
Poplar, The   60
Rainy Song   49
Reconnaissance   54
Red, Red Rose, A   114
Refugee in America   44
Requiem   157
Reunion, The   129
Rhapsody   156
River-Merchant's Wife: A Letter, The   120
Sailor   80
Saturday's Child   88
Sea Born   78
Sea Shell   81
Sketch   83
Smells   161
Son   24
Song, A   160
Song in the Front Yard, A   101
Song to Celia   115
Sonnet CXXX   122
Sound of Trees, The   58
Spring Grass   53
Spring in New Hampshire   52
Spring Reminiscence   47
Spring Thunder   46
Stanley Meets Mutesa   150
Strong Men   138
Tangerines   89
To a Winter Squirrel   76
To James   90
To Make a Prairie   21
Trade Winds   86
Travel   26
Travel   43

Tree at My Window   59
Tree Design, A   66
Treehouse, The   178
Trifle   20
Tropics in New York, The   167
Twelfth Night: Song of the Camels   72
Unknown Color, The   55
We Real Cool   106
We Wear the Mask   103
We'll Go No More A-Roving   113
When Dawn Comes to the City   30
When I Was One-and-Twenty   96
Wild Plum   65
Winning of the TV West, The   97
Your World   170
Youth   107

INDEX TO FIRST LINES

A lonely lake, a lonely shore,   75
A poem should be palpable and mute   168
A song is but a little thing,   154
A tree is more than a shadow   66
After the cloud embankments,   54
Against the day of sorrow   20
Although she feeds me bread of bitterness,   40
Arithmetic is where numbers fly like pigeons in and out of
your head.   108
Bananas ripe and green, and gingerroot,   167
Born of the sorrowful of heart,   141
Bowed by the weight of centuries he leans   144
Cross-legged on his bed,   24
Dark hills at evening in the west,   133
Day by day I float my paper boats one by one down the run-
ning stream   28

Do you remember 90
Down the dripping pathway dancing through the rain, 49
Drifting night in the Georgia pines, 158
Drink to me only with thine eyes, 115
Dust always blowing about the town, 21
Fear no more the heat o' th' sun, 179
He sat upon the rolling deck 80
He snuggles his fingers 50
Hear the sledges with the bells— 162
Hold fast to dreams 19
How do I love thee? Let me count the ways. 112
I am glad daylong for the gift of song, 156
I asked the heaven of stars 123
I broke my heart because of you, my dear; 170
I dream a world where man 29
I have sown beside all waters in my day. 93
I heard a bird at break of day 136
I know now 84
I loved the apple-sweetness of the air 129
I saw him once before 134
I shall not sing a May song. 136
I should like to rise and go 26
I walk down the garden paths, 116
I wandered lonely as a cloud 48
I wonder about trees. 58
If I can stop one heart from breaking, 140
In somewhat of a daze I lost the tangerines, 89
In the harbour, in the island, in the Spanish Seas, 86
In the June twilight, we looked without knowing why 68
Is there, for honest poverty, 142
It is portentous, and a thing of state 148
It looked extremely rocky for the Mudville nine that day, 98
It was six men of Indostan 73
I've often heard my mother say, 55
I've stayed in the front yard all my life. 101
John Henry told his Captain, 104

186

Let it be forgotten, as a flower is forgotten,   127
Listen. The wind is still,   46
Love, leave me like the light,   32
Music, when soft voices die,   124
My heart leaps up when I behold   55
My mistress' eyes are nothing like the sun;   122
My mother bore me in an island town,   78
My pathway lies through worse than death;   103
My Sorrow, when she's here with me,   130
"My sweet," you sang,   47
Nature's first green is gold,   56
Not born to the forest are we,   72
Not like the brazen giant of Greek fame,   35
Nothing happens only once,   172
Now as the train bears west,   36
Now does the golden tickseed bloom its last;   128
Now that he is safely dead   147
O my luve is like a red, red rose,   114
O what can ail thee, knight-at-arms,   22
Oh, long long   34
One summer's day a Fox was passing through   70
One, two, and three,   62
Out beyond the sunset, could I but find the way,   82
Sea Shell, Sea Shell,   81
She does not know   92
Slowly I smoke and hug my knee,   174
So, we'll go no more a-roving   113
Some are teethed on a silver spoon,   88
Speak gently, Spring, and make no sudden sound;   71
Spring grass, there is a dance to be danced for you.   53
Still and calm,   20
Strephon kissed me in the spring,   124
Such a time of it they had;   150
That is the way God made you.   76
The beauty of manhole covers—what of that?   42
The frogs were living happy as could be   94

The morns are meeker than they were, 127
The mountain and the squirrel 69
The quality of mercy is not strained; 141
The railroad track is miles away, 43
The shadows of the ships 83
The tired cars go grumbling by, 30
The trees along this city street, 64
The wise guys 109
There are words like *Freedom* 44
They are all gone away, 131
They are unholy who are born 65
They dragged you from homeland, 138
This is the debt I pay 176
Thou art the soul of a summer's day 160
To every man 178
To make a prairie it takes a clover and one bee— 21
Too green the springing April grass, 52
Tree at my window, window tree, 59
Under the wide and starry sky 157
We have tomorrow 107
We real cool. We 106
We wear the mask that grins and lies, 103
Well, son, I'll tell you: 177
What passing-bells for these who die as cattle? 173
When I come down to sleep death's endless night, 41
When I was one-and-twenty 96
When three, he fished these lakes, 146
When twilight comes to Prairie Street 97
While my hair was still cut straight my forehead 120
Whoever it was who brought the first wood and coal 132
Why do I curse the jazz of this hotel? 166
Why do you always stand there shivering? 60
Why is it that the poets tell 161
You hear the din and drone of birds 126
Your hands, Mandy Lou 37
Your world is as big as you make it. 170

ACKNOWLEDGMENTS

Grateful acknowledgment is made to the following poets, publishers, and other copyright holders for permission to include the poems in this anthology.

ALDINGTON: "The Poplar" by Richard Aldington reprinted by permission of the Ann Elmo Agency, Inc.

ALEXANDER: John T. Alexander and the Kansas City *Star* for "The Winning of the TV West."

AUSTIN: Houghton Mifflin for permission to reprint "The Grass on the Mountain" by Mary Austin from *American Rhythm*, copyright 1923, 1930.

BONTEMPS: "A Black Man Talks of Reaping," "Reconnaissance," and "A Tree Design," reprinted by permission of Harold Ober Associates, Inc. Copyright 1963 by Arna Bontemps.

BRAITHWAITE: "Rhapsody" reprinted by permission of Coward-McCann, Inc. from *Selected Poems* by William Stanley Braithwaite. Copyright by William Stanley Braithwaite.

BROOKS: "The Crazy Woman" copyright © 1960 by Gwendolyn Brooks Blakely, "A Song in the Front Yard" copyright 1945 by Gwendolyn Brooks Blakely, and "We Real Cool" copyright © 1959 by Gwendolyn Brooks Blakely from *Selected Poems* by Gwendolyn Brooks Blakely; "To a Winter Squirrel" (1965) from *In the Mecca* by Gwendolyn Brooks (Harper & Row, 1968). Reprinted by permission of Harper & Row, Publishers, Incorporated.

BROWN: "After Winter" and "Strong Men" reprinted by permission of Sterling A. Brown, from *Southern Road*, Harcourt, Brace and World, Inc., 1932.

BYNNER: "THE BATS" by Witter Bynner reprinted by permission of Alfred A. Knopf, Inc. from *Indian Earth*. Copyright 1929 by Alfred A. Knopf, Inc. and renewed 1957 by Witter Bynner.

COATSWORTH: "Twelfth Night: Song of the Camels" by Elizabeth Coatsworth reprinted by permission of the Macmillan Company from *Country Poems* copyright 1942 by Elizabeth Coatsworth.

CULLEN: "Epitaphs: For Paul Laurence Dunbar," "If You Should Go," and "Saturday's Child" from *On These I Stand* by Countee Cullen copyright, 1925 by Harper & Brothers; renewed 1953 by Ida M. Cullen; "Leaves" and "The Unknown Color" from *Copper Sun* by Countee Cullen copyright 1927 by Harper & Brothers; renewed 1955 by Ida M. Cullen; "Spring Reminiscence" from *Color* by Countee Cullen copyright 1925 by Harper & Brothers; renewed 1953 by Ida M. Cullen. Reprinted by permission of Harper & Row, Publishers, Inc.

DAVIS: Frank Marshall Davis for permission to reprint "Hands of a Brown Woman."

189

DODSON: Owen Dodson for permission to reprint "Circle One" and "The Reunion."

EASTMAN: Max Eastman for permission to reprint "Rainy Song" from *Poems of Five Decades* published by Harper & Brothers, 1954.

EMANUEL: James A. Emanuel for permission to reprint "Fishermen," "Son," and "The Treehouse."

FROST: "My November Guest," "Nothing Gold Can Stay," "A Peck of Gold," "The Sound of Trees," and "Tree at My Window" from *Complete Poems of Robert Frost*. Copyright 1916, 1923, 1928, 1934 by Holt, Rinehart and Winston, Inc. Copyright 1944, 1951, © 1962 by Robert Frost. Reprinted by permission of Holt, Rinehart and Winston, Inc.

HAYDEN: "O Daedalus, Fly Away Home" by Robert Hayden from *Selected Poems* copyright © 1966 by Robert Hayden. Reprinted by permission of October House Inc.

HINES: Carl W. Hines, Jr. for permission to reprint "Now That He Is Safely Dead."

HORNE: Frank Horne for permission to reprint "Kid Stuff" and "To James."

HUGHES: "Dreams" copyright 1932 by Langston Hughes, "I Dream a World" copyright 1945 by Langston Hughes, "I Thought It Was Tangiers I Wanted" copyright 1927 by Langston Hughes, published in *Opportunity*, December, 1927. "Mother to Son" copyright 1926 by Langston Hughes, "Refugee in America" copyright 1947 by Langston Hughes, "Sailor" copyright 1932 by Langston Hughes, and "Youth" copyright 1932 by Langston Hughes. Reprinted by permission of Harold Ober Associates Inc.

JOHNSON: "My City" from *Saint Peter Relates an Incident* by James Weldon Johnson copyright 1935 by James Weldon Johnson, copyright © renewed 1963 by Grace Nail Johnson. Reprinted by permission of The Viking Press, Inc.

KARANIKAS: "Autumn Flight" and "Tangerines" by permission of Alexander Karanikas.

LAUREN: "The Fox and the Grapes" and "The Frogs Who Wanted a King" from *Rainbow in the Sky* edited by Louis Untermeyer, copyright 1935 by Harcourt, Brace & World, Inc.; renewed 1963 by Louis Untermeyer, and reprinted by permission of the publishers.

LINDSAY: "Abraham Lincoln Walks at Midnight" reprinted with permission of The Macmillan Company from *Collected Poems* by Vachel Lindsay. Copyright 1914 by The Macmillan Company renewed 1942 by Elizabeth C. Lindsay. "The Jazz of This Hotel" from *Going to the Stars* by Vachel Lindsay copyright 1926 by D. Appleton & Company, affiliate of Meredith Press. Copyright renewed 1954 by Elizabeth C. Lindsay.

MCKAY: "America," "Spring in New Hampshire," "The Tropics in

New York," and "When Dawn Comes to the City" by Claude McKay reprinted by permission of Twayne Publishers, Inc.

MACLEISH: "Ars Poetica" by Archibald MacLeish reprinted by permission of Houghton Mifflin Company.

MASEFIELD: "The Golden City of St. Mary" and "Trade Winds" by John Masefield reprinted with permission of The Macmillan Company from *Poems* by John Masefield. Copyright 1916 by John Masefield renewed 1944 by John Masefield.

MILLAY: "City Trees" and "Travel" by Edna St. Vincent Millay from *Collected Poems*, Harper & Row. Copyright 1921, 1934, 1962 by Edna St. Vincent Millay and Norma Millay Ellis.

MONROE: "The Blue Ridge" by Harriet Monroe reprinted with permission of The Macmillan Company from *Chosen Poems* by Harriet Monroe. Copyright 1914, 1935 by The Macmillan Company. Copyright 1924 by Harriet Monroe.

MORLEY: "Smells" by Christopher Morley from *The Rocking Horse* by Christopher Morley. Copyright 1919, 1947 by Christopher Morley. Reprinted by permission of J.B. Lippincott Company.

OWEN: "Anthem for Doomed Youth" by Wilfred Owen from Wilfred Owen, *Collected Poems*. Copyright Chatto and Windus, Ltd. 1946 © 1963. Reprinted by permission of New Directions Publishing Corporation.

POUND: "The River-Merchant's Wife: A Letter" by Ezra Pound from Ezra Pound *Personae*. Copyright 1928, 1954 by Ezra Pound. Reprinted by permission of New Directions Publishing Corporation.

ROBINSON: E.A. Robinson "Ballade by the Fire" and "The House on the Hill" reprinted with the permission of Charles Scribner's Sons from *The Children of the Night* by Edwin Arlington Robinson (1897). "The Dark Hills" from *Collected Poems* by E.A. Robinson published by The Macmillan Company.

ROETHKE: "Night Journey" by Theodore Roethke copyright 1940 by Theodore Roethke from *The Collected Poems of Theodore Roethke*. Reprinted by permission of Doubleday & Company, Inc.

RUBADIRI: "Stanley Meets Mutesa" by James D. Rubadiri, reprinted from *Poems from Black Africa*, edited by Langston Hughes, by permission of Indiana University Press.

SANDBURG: Carl Sandburg "Arithmetic" from *Complete Poems* copyright 1950 by Carl Sandburg and "Spring Grass" from *Good Morning, America* copyright 1928, 1956 by Carl Sandburg reprinted by permission of Harcourt, Brace & World, Inc. "Sketch" from *Chicago Poems* by Carl Sandburg reprinted by permission of Holt, Rinehart & Winston, Inc.

SARETT: "Four Little Foxes" and "The Loon" from *Covenant With*

Earth: A Selection from the Poems of Lew Sarett. Edited and copyrighted 1956 by Alma Johnson Sarett, and published by the University of Florida Press. Reprinted by permission of Mrs. Sarett.

SAXE: "The Blind Men and the Elephant" by John Godfrey Saxe reprinted by permission of Houghton Mifflin Company.

SHAPIRO: "Manhole Covers" by Karl Shapiro. © Copyright 1962 by Karl Shapiro. Reprinted from *Selected Poems,* by Karl Shapiro, by permission of Rondom House, Inc. Originally appeared in *The New Yorker.*

TAGORE: "Paper Boats" by Rabindranath Tagore reprinted with permission of The Macmillan Company from *The Crescent Moon* by Rabindranath Tagore. Copyright 1913 by The Macmillan Company, renewed 1941 by Rabindranath Tagore.

TEASDALE: "Let It Be Forgotten" by Sara Teasdale reprinted with permission of The Macmillan Company from *Flame and Shadow* by Sara Teasdale. Copyright 1920 by The Macmillan Company renewed 1948 by Mamie T. Wheless. "The Look" and "Night Song at Amalfi" reprinted with permission of The Macmillan Company from *Rivers to the Sea* by Sara Teasdale. Copyright 1915 by The Macmillan Company renewed 1943 by Mamie T. Wheless.

VAN DOREN: "Spring Thunder" by Mark Van Doren from *Collected and New Poems: 1924-1963* by Mark Van Doren. Reprinted with permission by Hill & Wang.

Every effort has been made to trace the owners of copyright material in this book. Should any material have been included inadvertently without the permission of the copyright owner acknowledgment will be made in any future edition.